# SYNTHETIC ADHESIVES

*By*

Paul I. Smith

Author: *Principles and Processes of Light Leather Manufacture;
Glue and Gelatine;* First Class Diploma: *Leather Chemistry and Manufacture,* Leathersellers College, London:
City and Guilds of London Institute First Class
Certificates (Leather Manufacture).

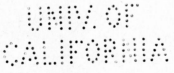

1943

CHEMICAL PUBLISHING CO., INC.

Brooklyn, N. Y.                    U. S. A.

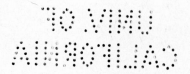

# PREFACE

S‌YNTHETIC adhesives, mostly of plastic origin, and produced
either as special commodities by new industrial chemical
undertakings or as profitable sidelines by well established
manufacturers of synthetic resins, are in great demand today, particularly by the aircraft, shipbuilding and allied industries.

The scope of synthetic adhesives has increased by leaps
and bounds during the last ten years and there are, today,
hundreds of different types of cements produced to solve
problems which before were considered to be without solution. Besides the "bread and butter" lines such as cold
or hot curing glues for plywood and improved wood production as well as for the assembly of wood structures,
chemically resistant cements are being manufactured for
making joints between rubber and metal; special adhesives
are also made for sticking plastics, glass, leather and fabrics
to all kinds of bases and there are special high dielectric
strength jointing materials for the electrical industry, lamp
basing and bristle setting cements, tasteless and odorless
adhesives for the food industry, sealing agents for non-
shattering glass, etc.

Synthetic adhesives are in direct competition with the
natural glues and gums for many applications and although
it is not claimed that they are always superior, there is no

iii

doubt that synthetic adhesives offer great advantages where speed of production is a primary factor and where there is a need for the maximum strength and reliability of joint coupled with high water-resistance, immunity to attack by fungi, etc. In the manufacture of plywood, synthetic resin glue enables bonding to be carried out in minutes instead of hours at temperatures of only 200 to 230° F. Many other examples of the great speed-up in production due to the use of synthetic adhesives could be quoted, but the proper place for such references is in the chapter dealing with applications.

One great practical advantage of the plastic type of cement over natural protein glue is that the former can be more easily modified to meet special requirements, e. g. urea formaldehyde resin may be cured or hardened in a short time or a relatively long time, or the joint may be made resistant to boiling water by merely altering the chemical constitution or strength of the acid hardener used in conjunction with the resin; vinyl cements are available in many different forms, each one being developed and made suitable for a particular application and cellulose nitrate, by modifying with other resins and plasticizers, can be formulated in a score or more ways.

The writer does not wish to imply that natural glues and gums are now out of use, on the contrary, they are of the greatest importance and will continue to be so for a large number of applications. Synthetic adhesives supplement but do not supplant the natural products.

The present volume should be considered as a primer or practical introduction to the subject rather than as an exhaustive catalogue of industrial adhesives. The author makes no claim of including all the synthetic cements and glues known to modern industry, but he has aimed at an adequate description of the main types of synthetic adhesives with due emphasis on their peculiar properties and main applications.

It is hoped that the appearance of this volume will be welcome to all users of industrial adhesives and afford useful practical information to men in a hurry to solve special problems. Purely scientific considerations such as the more advanced theories of adhesion, although of the greatest importance to physicists and research chemists, have not been given much space. The author's aim throughout has been to render the book useful as a main reference work and one which will tell the works manager or foreman what adhesive will do a certain job in the quickest time consistent with maximum strength and reliability of bond under normal or even abnormal working conditions.

PAUL I. SMITH

# INTRODUCTION

THERE is no hard and fast definition of an adhesive. The popular conception is that it is some kind of glue capable of sticking together two or more pieces of material. The term "glue" implies that it is a substance of sticky nature. Although in the main this conception is correct, it is necessary to point out that many substances possessing the property of sticking materials together cannot, by any stretch of imagination, be considered as glues. Professor J. W. McBain has shown that a wide range of pure substances can act as adhesives. Naphthalene, paraffin wax, etc., will give reasonably good joints between metals, and water, on freezing, makes excellent joints between wood surfaces.

In the present volume the author is confined to the consideration of synthetic adhesives commonly known as cements, glues, sealing and bonding agents, etc. These new types of adhesives will, under certain clearly defined conditions, enable many different materials such as wood, metal, plastics, glass, rubber, textiles, paper, etc., to be bonded with great speed and economy of labor and material. The joints produced are in many cases even stronger than the material itself.

There is no universal synthetic glue. This fact is not always fully appreciated. It should, however, be duly emphasized that the nature of the materials to be bonded, and this means character, condition and type of surface, and the purpose for which bonding is carried out must always influence the choice of adhesive. Generally speaking, each synthetic adhesive is developed for a certain limited range of uses, e. g. Tego for plywood and improved wood manufacture; urea formaldehyde resin for general wood assembly; phenolic varnishes for the binding of plywood and phenolic cements for joining up metal electrical units, lamp bases and bristle setting; chlorinated rubber cement for the bonding of rubber to metal, etc. In some cases, of course, the plastic adhesive can be modified to meet a number of different demands, thus polyvinyl cement is used with great success for bonding wood veneers (see Vidal process) and sticking many different types of plastics to one another and to glass.

Why is it that some substances possess this property of effecting a bond between two solid surfaces and others do not? Until a few years ago it was generally considered that the explanation was a mechanical one depending upon the embedding of the adhesive in the pores of the surface. The strength of joint effected was claimed to be due to the degree of penetration of the glue and its cohesive strength. In the light of research carried out during the last ten years or so, the mechanical theory is not regarded as affording an adequate explanation of adhesion, although it is accepted as an important contributory factor. The true nature of adhesion depends mainly upon forces exerted by mutually attractive surfaces. These forces, of which there are two kinds, polar and non-polar, are those exerted between atoms and molecules and commonly called secondary or cohesive forces.

Both adhesives and adherends can be roughly divided into polar and non-polar groups and such groups exercise varying degrees of attraction within themselves but polar groups will not attract non-polar ones and vice versa. The synthetic adhesives such as urea formaldehyde resin cement, phenolic dry gluefilm, and liquid phenolic glues are highly polar products and effect exceptionally strong bonds between surfaces of polar solids such as wood, but are unsatisfactory for bonding together non-polar materials, e. g. metals, plastics, glass, etc.

It is emphasised that in making the statement that polar adhesives will stick only to polar solids and vice versa it is assumed that reference is made to pure or simple substances. In the case of mixtures or complex materials the range of adhesive action is considerably enlarged. The addition of rubber compounds (non-polar) to phenolic varnishes (polar) produces a more versatile air-drying adhesive but one which has a lower bonding strength than the straight phenol formaldehyde resin glue cured or polymerized by the application of heat. The strongest joints are generally effected when adhesive and adherend belong to the same polar group. Changes in the nature of the cohesive forces between surfaces induced by physical or chemical action have profound effect on their adhesion. In the case of wood which has been over-heated there is a decided change in the surface polarity from polar to non-polar which means that standard polar synthetic glues are of no practical use.

Joint strength therefore depends on two vital factors:
1. Type or condition of adhesive.
2. Type or condition of adherend.

The two are closely related and successful adhesive action can only be ensured if the maximum cohesive forces are exerted between the surfaces. The purely mechanical side of adhesion must also be taken into account when assessing the possibility of effecting strong joints between surfaces. Not only must the surfaces be rendered fully receptive to the adhesive, but the materials to be joined must comply in all particulars with requirements laid down such as optimum moisture content.

The requirements of a good industrial adhesive may be usefully considered under the following main headings:

1. Maximum strength of bond
2. Minimum setting or drying time
3. Ease and rapidity of application
4. Ability of the bond to resist the stresses and strains required by the particular assembly and to retain its strength for long periods and under unfavorable conditions of humidity or increased temperature
5. Economical in use
6. Low working cost
7. Good keeping qualities and uniformity and regularity of supplies
8. Freedom from health hazards, particularly as regards solvents
9. Freedom from objectionable corrosive or coloring action on materials to be bonded.

When considering these it is necessary to regard them as inter-related. Thus No. 1 should be reviewed alongside with No. 4. An adhesive must be able to provide a strong joint able to retain its strength indefinitely. Any weakening due to absorption of moisture, cracking due to strain, vibration or chemical deterioration makes the strongest joint a potential weakness. There is no adhesive in production able to fulfil all the requirements named, but some of the synthetic adhesives do come very close to the ideal for certain types of work. Tego is excellent for hot bonding but quite unsuitable for cold bonding, whereas a urea formaldehyde resin cement gives high-strength joints in the cold but this adhesive sometimes presents difficulties in application and does not keep for many hours when mixed ready for use.

It will thus be seen that whereas an adhesive might under one set of working conditions appear very good indeed, under new conditions it may be troublesome in use or definitely unsuitable.

The manufacturer can usually adapt his plant and processes to a new adhesive if it possesses quite exceptional properties such as very high bonding strength and very low setting or drying time, but otherwise the adhesive must be able to be readily adapted to the plant and processes.

The main types of synthetic adhesives to be described in this book will be:

1. Phenol-formaldehyde resins such as dry gluefilm, liquid varnishes and special cements
2. Urea-formaldehyde resin glues in liquid and solid forms
3. Polyvinyl adhesives
4. Cellulose ester products
5. Acrylic adhesives
6. Polystyrol cements
7. Alkyd sealing agents
8. Chlorinated rubber compounds
9. Synthetic rubber cements.

The first two classes, which constitute the thermo-setting group, are the most important, particularly for plywood and improved wood manufacture, but the range of thermo-plastic cements is naturally more extensive and developments have taken place during the last few years which now render their usefulness in industry much appreciated.

# CONTENTS

xiii

# Chapter I

# DRY GLUEFILM, PHENOL-FORMALDEHYDE RESIN

PHENOLIC resin impregnated tissue paper, commonly known as dry gluefilm has a resin content varying from approximately 37–49% and a thickness from 0.003 to 0.01 inch. The film is usually translucent in appearance but, in the case of the heavier type, it may be opaque, and possesses a strong phenolic smell.

The general principle of manufacture consists of reacting phenol, or mixtures of phenol and cresylic acid, and formaldehyde in molar proportions using a small amount of sodium hydroxide as a catalyst. The resultant resinoid (without being carried to the point of water separation) is impregnated on a tissue paper carrier some 0.001 inch thick (or thicker depending on the purpose) giving an actual resin film of little more than 0.002 inches thick (average). The gluefilm is perfectly dry and non-sticky to handle, but in the hot press the resinous deposit softens and flows and forms a bond so strong that the greatest strength of the material is at the glue-line, provided, of course, that the materials to be bonded together are polar.

Commercial forms of dry gluefilm of phenolic origin are available for use as rolls, each consisting of a continuous

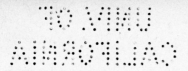

sheet, usually about 4 ft. wide, and 4000 ft. long. It is, however, possible to produce the film in widths of 74 inches or even more. About 1 lb. weight of the film will cover a wood area of 80 to 85 sq. ft.

## Main Advantages

Practical advantages claimed for dry gluefilm as typified by Tego, the best known of all phenolic resin films, are:

1. Very high strength and tenacity, the bond being stronger than the wood itself.
2. Permanent and non-aging properties of the bond.
3. Good resistance to stresses and strains and to vibration. There is no "crazing" along the glue-line and therefore no risk of breakdown due to loss of adhesive power under strain.
3a. Use of dry gluefilm enables curved sections and shapes to be economically produced.
4. Ability to afford some compensation for unsuspected weakness of veneers.
5. Impervious to moisture under all conditions of service.
6. Unaffected by either heat or cold. The bond, which is infusible, will withstand boiling water without any signs of injury. Alternate changes of temperature have no injurious effect on the structure of the glue-line.
7. Complete immunity to attack by fungi and bacteria.
8. The dry gluefilm prevents face veneers from checking and splitting.
9. Neutral reaction of the dry gluefilm means freedom from corrosion of materials to be stuck and also metal equipment.
10. Use of the dry gluefilm results in an appreciable saving on labor owing to reduced handling, sanding

and pressing time. Another important factor in these days of crowded warehouse accommodation is that the bonded plywood needs no period of conditioning before use but can be taken into service straight away. This, of course, saves a great deal of time and speeds up the production of essential war goods.

11. Moisture content of film is nil and therefore liability of plywood to swell and warp is reduced to a minimum. No drying out of the plywood after bonding is necessary although in some cases a re-conditioning to replace moisture lost during hot pressing may be desirable.

12. Economy of gluefilm. The material keeps indefinitely under suitable conditions of storage and every scrap of tissue can be utilized.

13. Perfect uniformity of quality and thickness of film.

## Moisture Content and Pressing Conditions

The main disadvantage of dry gluefilm is that the hot bonding process must be used which entails the installation of large and expensive presses. Another disadvantage is that for the best results the veneers must be properly conditioned to a successful moisture content, approximately 10%, if really successful results are to be guaranteed. The shear strength of bonded wood is greatly influenced by the moisture content of the wood.

It is necessary to standardize the moisture content throughout the wood. There must be no wide difference between the moisture content in the middle of the section and that on the surface. If differences of 20–25% exist, as they sometimes do, this will mean a variable shear strength and the possibility of a breakdown due to internal stresses. If the moisture content is too low, say 3 or 4%, the glue-line becomes brittle and ultimate strength is impaired. If, on the other hand, the moisture content is too high this is responsible for the uneven flow of resin (due to poor distribution of heat which is taken up in evaporating moisture) and patchy or uneven bonding strength. Working with a platen temperature of 300° F., specific pressure 150–200 lbs. per sq. in. and thickness of core ¼ inch. Thomas D. Perry and Martin F. Bretl, A. S. M. E. Transactions, January, 1938, found that the temperatures attained after 20 minutes pressing at a penetration depth of ⅜ inch were approx. 293° F. for plies containing 0 to 1% moisture; 240° F. for 7 to 9% and 219° F. for 13 to 15% moisture. Figures given for a three ply 4.8 mm. birch bonded with British Tego at 285° F. and 280 lbs. per sq. in. pressure, are of considerable interest. At 2% moisture the wood had a shear strength of 200 lbs. per sq. in.; at 6% moisture the shear strength increased to 450 lbs. per sq. in.; 10% moisture brought the figure up to 460 but at 12% it dropped to 410 and at 16% moisture to 325 lbs. per sq. in. Another important factor in relation to moisture content of wood to be hot pressed is that compression largely depends on moisture content. Although compression (well below actual crushing) increases the strength of the bonded wood it should be avoided whenever plywood is to be shaped or bent after bonding. Perry and Bretl give the following data regarding percentage of compression in plywood with graduated pressure and variable moisture content. Taking the case of ³⁄₁₆ inch birch at 0–1% moisture content the compression at 150 lbs. pressure is 4.13% and 4.64% at 250 lbs. pressure, whereas when the moisture content is increased to 11% the compression at 150 lbs. per sq. in. pressure is 11.11% and 24.0% at 250 lbs. pressure. (Plate temperature in all cases 300° F.). The compression obtained when using softwood veneers is very marked at different moisture contents. In the case of $\frac{3}{16}$ inch (1% moisture) fir at 200 lbs. per sq. in. pressure the compression is 6.56% whereas if the moisture is increased to 8.0% the compression is also increased to 32.0%.

It will be apparent from the above that the success of hot bonding technique depends to a large degree upon the scientific control of moisture and necessitates most careful conditioning of the plies. Increase in moisture content must retard penetration of heat which means that the resin is not properly softened and allowed to flow along the glue-line subsequent to curing or hardening. The thicker the veneer the slower will be the penetration of heat and if there is a fairly large content of moisture present, the bonding must inevitably be poor. In those cases where the glue-line is at a distance of $\frac{3}{8}$ inches or more from the platen and the plies contain a relatively high percentage of moisture, there must be an increase in pressing time to effect proper bonding. The time factor, therefore, depends on the distance to the farthest glue line and moisture content of the veneers. In connection with increase in the time of hot pressing it is necessary to bear in mind that by subjecting the surface of the wood to the continued platen temperature there may occur undesirable changes in the physical properties of the wood. Heat treatment of wood changes its polarity and renders its surfaces difficult to bond with polar glues. That is why hot pressed plywood cannot be always successfully glued up with dry gluefilm or urea-formaldehyde.

## Temperature of Bonding

Temperature of bonding must always be considered in relation to pressure, both being vital factors in bonding. The time necessary for the actual application of both heat and pressure is recommended to be six minutes plus one minute for each millimeter of thickness of the plywood measured to the innermost glue-layer. The pressure is not standard but varies according to the type of wood to be bonded.

Coniferous woods require the lowest pressure, 120–140 lbs. per sq. in. and high density woods 150–300 lbs. per sq. in. Low density woods for rotary core stock or soft wood cores need a pressure of 140–150 lbs. per sq. in. It is, however, impossible, or rather undesirable to lay down any hard and fast rules for pressure; woods in the same series sometimes require different pressures and the manufacturer can only arrive at an optimum pressure by experiment. Perry and Bretl found that the maximum shear strength (wet) 420 lbs. per sq. in. was obtained using $\frac{3}{16}$ inch birch veneers (7 to 9% moisture) with a platen temperature of 320° F. and specific pressure of 250 lbs. per sq. in. and allowing a bonding time of ten minutes.

## Conditions Governing Successful Bonding

These may be summarized as follows :—

1. Moisture content of wood adjacent to the glue-line
2. Temperature at bonding or glue-line
3. The specific pressure as contrasted with pump or piston pressure
4. Time under full pressure.

In principle, the standard method of using dry gluefilm is comparatively simple, merely consisting of building up a stack of veneers and gluefilm and effecting bonding by application of heat and pressure. The veneers are taken out of the storage or conditioning room and the sheets of gluefilm necessary to inter-leave the stack cut to size with a sheet cutting machine or by the hand. Odd pieces, that is, off cuts of gluefilm may be used so that there is no wastage. The press charge is then built up immediately using $\frac{1}{16}$ to $\frac{1}{8}$ in. thick aluminum cauls or sheets on both sides of each assembled stack of veneers and gluefilm. The press is then closed for a period varying from 3 to 15 minutes, pressure 150–350 lbs. per sq. in. and a temperature of 275 to 325° F. The time lag after closing the press and curing must not be longer than 1½ minutes and should preferably be one minute. On release from the press, the made-up wood or plywood is cooled off and then put into work.

## Durability

The durability of wood bonded with dry gluefilm is of the highest order. Experiments on Tego bonded plywood carried out by one manufacturer show the extraordinary resistance of the wood to strong deteriorating influence. Test panels were steamed for two weeks, put in a low temperature compartment of an electric icebox for two weeks and then dried out on a steam radiator for several weeks. Even after all these exposures there was no evidence of deterioration, warping or lateral movement of the veneers, and the surface of the plywood did not check in any way. Evidence provided by manufacturers whose stock suffered from flood exposures shows that Tego bonded plywood is able to withstand the most severe conditions. Resinous Products and Chemical Co., Inc. report that the prolonged heavy floods of the Ohio river in February, 1937, gave an unforeseen test of plywood in the Louisville area, especially since intermittent freezing occurred. At one plant, a great deal of Tego 2-ply and an inlaid table top were trapped in a flooded room for two weeks. These were later dried, cleaned and found entirely sound. It should be noted that plywood bonded with phenolic dry gluefilm will resist boiling in water almost indefinitely, whereas boiling for half an hour will de-laminate most other adhesives.

The dry gluefilm is, as mentioned previously, supplied to

the trade in the form of heavy rolls which are usually packed in plywood drums rimmed with metal. These drums should be allowed to stand upright and stored under dry conditions, not damp or warm.

Before closing this chapter it should be mentioned that apart from the use of phenolic resin dry gluefilm for plywood manufacture it is now extensively employed for improved or high-density wood. A special chapter is devoted to applications of this material later on in the book.

Types of Tego bonded wood. The piece in the beaker of water shows no swelling or distortion after a prolonged immersion.

9

Example of the type of modern furniture, suite in "Birds-Eye" Maple with bands of Indian Laurel, produced with the aid of Tego film instead of animal glue for veneering.

CHAPTER II

# PHENOL-FORMALDEHYDE LIQUID
# AND SOLID GLUES

THE conventional type of phenolic glues consists of high-resin-content spirit solutions, which usually contain catalysts able to promote rapid hardening of the resin under heat and pressure. These glues may be used at the high viscosity supplied by the manufacturer or adapted for use by addition of suitable solvents, generally industrial alcohol. The nature of the bond effected may be altered by the use of special additives such as linseed oil, china wood oil, ester gum and rubber or rubber derivatives which increase the elasticity and drying rate of the adhesives.

These standard liquid glues all require both heat and pressure to achieve satisfactory bonding. In some cases the pressure may be somewhat lower than is customary with dry gluefilm, but the temperature is usually about 250° F.; curing time in the press is less.

These spirit-soluble resin adhesives are now being used in the manufacture of plywood and are readily adaptable to standard glue spreading methods and machinery. Unlike casein or the urea-formaldehyde glues, the phenol-formaldehyde resin solution can be left in the spreader indefinitely with-

11

out fear of premature hardening. This itself is a considerable practical advantage and facilitates peak production figures. General method of using the glue is practically the same as with wet glue. The veneers have to contain an optimum percentage of moisture, approximately 6 to 7%. According to Karl Kopplin of Roddis Lumber and Veneer Co., in a paper read before the American Society of Mechanical Engineers, September 23rd, 1938, the bond obtained by the liquid phenolic glue is highly resistant to water, even boiling water, insects and fungi. Tests carried out on various types of plywood showed an increase in shear strength of liquid resin over dry film of 17.1% to 23.3% depending on the bonding time, the highest figure being secured with only four minutes setting. Increase in fungi shear strength of liquid resin over dry gluefilm was 10%. Kopplin states that the short time necessary to effect perfect hardening is particularly good. On testing, a four minute cure was found ample for all commercial or aircraft purposes, being equal to a nine minute dry film cure.

Liquid (spirit) phenolic glue may be used in two ways:

1. The glue can be applied to the surfaces to be bonded and after allowing the adhesive to become tacky, bonding can take place straight away.

2. The glue can be applied to the wood layers and allowed to dry off. This means that veneers, etc., can be coated with adhesive, dried off and put into store for two or three weeks before pressing. This is a practice which is sometimes very useful as it enables considerable stocks to be built up and thus prevents delay during bonding. The cure temperature is usually 200 to 250° F. and the pressure from 150 to 250 lbs. per sq. in. depending on the type of wood to be bonded.

The main disadvantage of the spirit soluble phenolic glue

is that it is relatively expensive and proves somewhat danger-
ous in work.

## Water Soluble Phenolic Glues

In general use today are several excellent water soluble
phenolic glues which are very economical in use, safe to
handle and readily adaptable to cold bonding. In the latter
case use is made of catalysts which enable the bonds to
approach hot pressed bonds in durability and moisture resistance, and make possible 100% resin bonding, particularly
in constructions where the use of hot pressing is unpractical.

The adhesive, Uformite 430 produced by Resinous Products and Chemical Co., Inc., is an excellent example of a
water-soluble phenolic resin glue which may be used either
as a cold bonding adhesive, i.e., at a temperature of 70° F.
or for hot pressing, with or without various extenders.

The glue is supplied as a milky liquid, specific gravity
1.32, containing 68–72% solids in water. Being chemically
reactive, it tends to thicken slightly upon ageing, but the
viscosity can be lowered to any working range desired by
dilution with small amounts of water. The viscosity of
the material is claimed by the manufacturers to have no
effect on the quality of the resulting bond. The resinous
solution has a useful life of more than three months provided it is kept from elevated temperatures or freezing. For
setting purposes the cure of the resin is accelerated by means
of a special catalyst; usually available as a free flowing
liquid.

The glue and catalyst when used for cold bonding may
be employed alone, or in conjunction with flour as an extender where it is desired to reduce the cost of the adhesive
and where a diminution in bonding strength is permitted.
For most types of work, the following mixture is recommended for Uformite 430.

| Uformite 430 | 1000 parts |
| Flour | 70 parts |
| Water | 60 parts |
| Catalyst Z | 10 parts |

The method of preparing the mix is simple. The catalyst is added slowly to the glue accompanied by constant stirring. The flour is then added and the mass thoroughly mixed. The working life of the made-up glue is approximately 6 hours and should be put into work without delay using standard glue spreading machinery. Pressure is carried out with the aid of clamps able to exercise a pressure of 100 lbs. per sq. in. or over. Higher pressures (up to 200 lbs. per sq. in.) may be desirable. Head blocks should be as nearly the same size as the sawn core block as possible, otherwise deflection of the "I" may result, giving insufficient pressure in the center of the block. Clamps should be well tightened.

The time required before removal from clamps varies with the temperature at which the bundles are maintained. For best results the manufacturers recommend that the clamped bundles be placed in a drying kiln at 110–140° F. overnight before removing clamps. The table below gives the time required in clamps at various temperatures.

| Temperature | Time in Clamps |
|---|---|
| 70° F. | 24 to 48 hours |
| 80° F. | 24 hours |
| 100° F. | 16 hours |
| 120° F. | 8 hours |

It is emphasized that although these resin plus catalyst solutions are very useful for cold bonding this cannot give such good results as hot bonding. When phenolic resin water-soluble glue is used for hot pressing in the same way as the solvent solution then it may be employed with or without extender. If employed with extender, larger amounts of this can be used than would be possible in the case of cold bonding.

## Aqueous Solutions of Phenolic Resin for Compressed Wood

Recent experiments by the Forest Products Research Laboratory (A. J. Stamin and R. M. Seborg, Trans. Amer. Inst. Chem. Engineers, 1941) show that aqueous solutions of special phenolic resins, practically unpolymerized phenol-formaldehyde resin forming mixtures with a pH of 8 which are soluble in water in all proportions are of great value as joint impregnation and adhesive agents. The solution of resin is allowed to diffuse into green veneer direct from the cutter knives by merely soaking it in an aqueous solution of the mixture. Time required varies as the square of the thickness of the veneers, directly as the specific gravity of the wood and inversely with the moisture content of the wood and the temperature. Green sweetgum veneers of $\frac{1}{32}$ in. absorbed approximately 40% of the dry weight of resin-forming constituents from a 50% solution of Bakelite Resinoid XR 5995 by diffusion in 1 hour at 100° F.

After drying the veneers to a standard moisture content, they can be bonded together and simultaneously compressed at a pressure of 250 lbs. per sq. in. The investigators found that spruce cottonwood or aspen could be compressed to one half of their original thickness. If there is insufficient resin present on or near the surface of the impregnated veneers to effect bonding, Tego film may be used. The compressed wood made in this way, using a range of pressure from 250 lbs. per sq. in. to 1,200 lbs. per sq. in. and a temperature of 300 to 320° F., time 15 to 30 minutes per inch of original thickness of wood, has a smooth water-resistant surface with a sword hardness varying from 65 to 90 compared with 100 for plate glass. The specific gravity is 1.3, tensile strength parallel to grain

40,000 lbs. per sq. in.; maximum crushing strength with compression parallel to grain over 20,000 and modulus of elasticity values for the previous three properties ranging from 4 to 5 millions.

## Phenolic Resins In Powder Form

There are now three types of these on the market. The first is a powdered resin which dissolves readily in water and makes a glue able to produce waterproof and boilproof bonds by the standard hot pressing process, optimum temperature being approximately 300° F.

The second type is developed for use with large quantities of blood or other protein matter at about 240° F. particularly with Douglas fir, hitherto a somewhat difficult material to bond. The third type, which can be used at temperatures of 230 to 250° F. produces an exceedingly strong joint and both powder and aqueous solution are very stable, the latter over a wide range of pH.

These water-soluble phenolic resins are of the greatest practical importance because of their ecomony in use, freedom from any kind of fire hazard, ease of storage and shipping and the high strength of joint effected.

## Special Liquid Phenolic Glues For Aeronautical Applications

Comparatively new products, certain specially developed catalysts are now being used in the building of improved wood American aircraft. Comparative shear and compression tests were made by the manufacturer of Timm training planes on joints bonded with plastic resin and other glues. Thus, a wing rib cap strip having 1 sq. in. of effective area bonded with casein glue, when placed in tension with the rib proper, sheared from the rib at 290 lbs. per sq. in. An equivalent cap bonded with Timm special resin set cold and not heat-treated, parted from the rib at a tension of 316 lbs. A duplicate cap, similarly bonded with the resin and then heat-treated broke away at 490 lbs. per sq. in. As will be seen from the above, baking or local heat-treatment does result in a considerable increase in the strength of the joints, but, at the same time, the ability of the phenolic glue to set hard is of the greatest practical importance, as with it, it may be possible to repair wooden planes, directly on the field.

## MISCELLANEOUS PHENOLIC CEMENTS

### Phenolic Baking Cements

Phenolic resin cements are now extensively employed in the manufacture of various kinds of electrical apparatus, such as resistors, commutators, transformers, etc. Their best known application is probably for basing electrical light bulbs and radio tubes as well as brushes.

The resins are usually available as granular powders which require mixing with industrial alcohol to secure a cement of the required viscosity and also as highly viscous or paste-like cements with a resin content of 75–85% and a viscosity at 25° C. of about 4,000 centipoises. They may be loaded with mineral or plastic fillers where it is necessary to use it for stopping, bridging gaps or to reduce shrinkage of the film, etc. The fillers employed vary considerably. Thus, chalk, siliceous earth, wood flour, asbestos and phenolic moulding powders may all be used for special jobs, particularly the cementing of electrical parts where a bond not liable to track is needed. When fully baked and polymerized the bond effected with these phenolic cements is hard, non-hygroscopic, electrically insulating, highly resistant to chemical attack, immune to the solubilising effect of solvents and able to withstand relatively high temperatures up to 180° C. without charring.

## Phenolic Resin Putty Or Resin Cement

Mixtures of phenolic resin and asbestos can be mixed in situ with 30% alcoholic solution of sulphuric acid (the catalyst) and made into a cement for applying to rough wood, dried silicate cement and rubber coated metal surfaces. The best known cement in use in the U. S. A. is Havegit. Besides asbestos, other fillers are employed, such as powdered quartz, graphite, kieselguhr, talc, resin, scrap, etc. The liquid resin is mixed with the filler to form a putty-like mass of the required consistency and prior to use needs thorough mixing with the alcoholic acid solution. It is usually applied to the surface to be protected with a hard-wood trowel. Considerable heat is generated after mixing the acid catalyst with the resin mixture and the temperature gives a reliable indication of the efficacy of the catalyst. It is claimed that the optimum amount of acid gives a temperature of 50° C. within 15 to 30 minutes of mixing.

Before coating metal or silicate cement surfaces with the above cement, it is advisable to protect it with a rubber coating to prevent acid corrosion from the catalyst present in the phenolic mixture. The usual protective coating consists of a straight rubber solution, but better results are obtained by the use of a chlorinated rubber finish. The latter can be made by mixing 2 parts of chlorinated rubber with 1 part of plasticiser and 0.75 parts of resin and thinning down with solvent as required.

## Phenolic Resin Rubber Cements

Commercial phenolic resin rubber cements may have a composition of 15% total solids and 85% volatile solvents and an acid value, expressed in terms of mgms KOH per gm of resinous base, of 8.5. These cements are air-drying and find many applications where quick drying and flexible film is required. They will stick ordinarily incompatible materials such as phenolic laminated paper and even plywood.

## Special Phenol Adhesives

Several phenolic resin glues have been introduced during the last few years for special purposes, such as bonding asbestos to sheet steel, rubber to metal or cellulose acetate materials; plastic moulded parts, porcelain enamelled parts, etc. Of particular interest is the 5116 Resin Adhesive made by General Plastics Inc., which is claimed to be unaffected by water, moderate heat, alkalies and mild acids. Used as a coating, the adhesive withstands a 50% caustic soda solution indefinitely, retains its bonding strength up to 100° C. Softening point between 115 and 120° C. (A. S. T. M.)

Synthetic resin (phenolic) is employed as an addition to bonding mixtures for cork and cork compositions. Brit. Pat. 482,539 mentions the following formula:—2 lbs. of tung oil-glue glycerin mixture (made with 4 lbs. of glycerin, 1 lb. of bodied tung oil and 1 lb. of glue), 1 lb. of phenolic resin and 4 ozs. of hexamethylenetetramine. 3 lbs. of the binder are used to coat 12 lbs. to 13 lbs. of cork granules.

A tile covered stirrer for use in the chemical industry. This stirrer is, of course, in constant rotation and the tiles hold very well using an acid-resisting phenolic resin cement.

20

## Chapter III

# UREA-FORMALDEHYDE GLUES

---

THE so-called U. F. glues consist essentially of two basic ingredients:—The actual urea or thiourea resin itself which is the real bonding agent and the catalyst or hardener, usually a weak acid or a salt of strong acid or mixture of salts freely soluble in water, also certain organic materials such as melamine, able to promote the rapid polymerisation or hardening of the resin. In some cases the resin is in the form of a heavy syrup and the hardener as a colored liquid of water-like consistency. In other cases the glue is available in powder form, which contains both resin and hardener, and it only requires dissolving in a fixed amount of water to make it immediately available for use. There are also powdered urea-formaldehyde glues without hardeners incorporated, these being issued separately owing to the needs of manufacturers for different types, such as quick-setting and slow-setting adhesives, or adhesives resistant to boiling water. It should be remembered that the rate of setting or curing is in direct relation to the strength of the catalyst and, to a lesser extent, to the temperature. Filling agents such as rye flour and certain inorganic materials are often added to the made-up adhesive to extend it and thus render it more economical in use. Such filling agents can only be used where a slight diminution of physical strength is permissible.

21

The U. F. resin itself seldom varies and one type only is available for all types of bonding. As mentioned above, the hardener, either in the liquid or solid form, is usually available in several different grades developed specifically for certain applications where maximum strength of joint, maximum water resistance, maximum heat resistance, etc., are required.

Main advantages of U. F. glues are as follows:

1. Strength of bond and durability comparable to the best produced by hot bonding.
2. Ready adaptability to assembly work in aircraft, shipbuilding and other war industries where speed of production is all important.
3. Low temperature and pressure of bonding with U. F. glues have no case hardening effects on the top veneers.
4. Even appreciable differences in the moisture content of veneers and cores used in the manufacture of aeronautical and other types of plywood are not of great importance. The range of water permissible is stated by some manufacturers to be 0–25%.
5. Reasonably low water content of the U. F. glue when compared with animal and other natural glues ensures freedom from twisting or distortion in the completed structure.
6. Absolute immunity to attack by mold or fungus.

The disadvantages are mainly as follows:

1. In the case of liquid U. F. glues the resin itself has a comparatively short life, that is, 2–3 months under favorable conditions of storage. Solid glues will keep as long as a year.
2. The made-up adhesive or mixture of glue and hardener only keeps a few hours before setting.

3. Great care should be taken to see that the glues are mixed in scrupulously clean non-metallic containers as small amounts of impurities are known to act as catalysts and promote premature polymerization. Special precaution must always be taken if casein glues are used in the same shop as U. F. glues. The former adhesives are very alkaline and therefore liable to cause rapid setting of the U. F. resin.

These disadvantages, although apparently rather serious, can be overcome by careful management. Modern U. F. glues are today recognized as being of the greatest importance to modern industry.

## Strength of U. F. Glue Joints

The breaking load of a joint effected with a good U. F. glue is approximately 25 to 30% higher than with a good casein glue. Tests carried out with well known industrial U. F. adhesives show that in all cases their strength exceeds the shear strength of the woods. It is, however, pointed out that since in some standard strength tests there is a certain amount of tension at right angles to the plane of the joint, complete wood failure does not invariably result. The manufacturers of the British material "Aerolite" point out that the so-called standard tests are not all satisfactory as tests of glue strength, as will be realized when it is stated that the same glue with the same wood will show a strength of 1,400 lbs. per sq. in. when tested in accordance with the British Specifications D. T. D. Spec. 335, and about 425 lbs. per sq. in. for 3 ply, 6 mm. thickness when tested in accordance with British Standard Specifications 4V3. It is sometimes thought that since both specifications require the line of action of applied force to be in the plane of the joint, only shearing forces are set up; but this is not so, because lack of stiffness in the test pieces allows bending to take place. In D. T. D. 335, the specimens are ⅜ ins. thick or even less, thus 335 test gives the highest figure.

U. F. bonded plywood complies in all particulars with U. S. (Aircraft Airworthiness Section Civil Aeronautics Authority; approved by C. A. A. 3/4/41) and British Government Ministry of Aircraft Production specifications and will stand up to the usual 3 hour boiling test without breakdown. Figures for a standard U. F. glue show a shear strength of 343 lbs. (average) for original plywood (birch 3 ply 1½ mm.) and 275 lbs. (average) for wood tested immediately after 3 hours boiling. Typical shear tests carried out on specimens with a 20/1000 in cement layer of Kaurit W. (Beetle Cement) are as follows:

*Dry Test*   Specimens tested 72 hours after cementing.
                1,320 lbs. per sq. in.    Cement failure with fibres
                1,600 lbs. per sq. in.    Cement failure with fibres
                1,187 lbs. per sq. in.    Wood failure

    Average  1,369

*Wet Test*   Specimens tested wet after 24 hours immersion in water.
                1,526 lbs. per sq. in.    Cement failure with fibres
                1,206 lbs. per sq. in.    Cement failure with fibres
                1,290 lbs. per sq. in.    Wood failure

    Average  1,341

Tests carried out in Germany in 1938 on U. F. bonded wooden constructions produced at the Spandau works of the Auto-Union A. G. show that the tensile strength of the plywood is approximately 335 lbs. per sq. in. dry, about 284 damp and about 227 wet. In VDI. Zeits., Vol. 83, p. 193, Feb. 18th, 1939, details are given on the special experiments made on the wooden stress-carrying car body assembled by the use of U. F. glue. It is stated that an inclined plane was erected, down which fully weighted cars were allowed to run. At the end of the ramp where the cars were travelling at 38 m.p.h. the track was tilted to an angle of 60° which forced them to capsize and turn several somersaults on a hard floor. The low centre of gravity made the cars end up on their wheels and in this position they ran up against a wall of sandbags. The resultant damage was of a minor nature such as dented mudguards, torn water connections and twisted headlamps, but in no case was there any damage to the bodies themselves. In every instance all windows and doors could be worked, steering wheels and gears could all be moved as before and the engines worked faultlessly. The cars left the test ground under their own power. These trials showed that the timber and glue construction used would withstand strains of an exceptional character such as would rarely occur in normal use, but might be likely to be experienced in war. It is understood that extensive use is being made of U. F. glues by Auto-Union A. G. in the construction of army trucks.

## Method of Handling

Modern solid U. F. glues should be prepared for use by slowly adding the resin to the water with careful stirring, until a smooth, uniform paste is obtained. In the case of one well known U. F. solid glue, Uformite CB–550, 70 pounds of glue require mixing with 2½ to 3 gallons of cold water. It should be remembered that in those cases where the glue and hardener are combined, the setting of the resin commences immediately after solution is effected and a working life of only 4 hours at a temperature of 70° F. can be assured. Batches of glue must, therefore, be made at intervals according to the flow of work. All mechanical mixers and containers used for handling U. F. glues should be washed out with plenty of warm water immediately after use to prevent the formation of solid resin on the surface. It is important that all containers and mixing vessels should be of iron, tin, wood, glass or earthenware but not copper or brass. Syrup glues do not require the addition of any water but are ready for use.

## Spreading

Ordinary glue spreaders are quite successful for all U. F. glues and those with slightly grooved rubber rollers give the best results. Brushes may also be used provided they are perfectly clean. The amount of adhesive per sq. ft. of wood to be bonded depends largely on the species of wood, hard woods requiring less glue than soft woods. Normally, liquid (Uformite CB–500) spreads in the range of 35–40 lbs. per 1,000 feet are adequate. Generous spreads should be used on end-grain wood, whereas smooth, side-grained surfaces may be satisfactorily bonded with lower spreads.

The manufacturers state that the rule should be that the aim in spreading is to cover completely and render tacky the surfaces to be bonded up to the time pressure is applied. The most difficult bonding condition is very soft wood against one much denser, such as spruce to maple, since the adhesive tends to flow into the more porous wood. In this case precoating and partial drying of the harder surface prior to normal glue spreading before pressure is recommended.

The surface of wood to be glued should not be too smooth and polished especially in very hard woods. Ordinary planer work or knife cut veneer is just right. Smooth saw cuts with a minimum of tooth marks are satisfactory. If it is necessary to work on very dense polished surfaces some roughening of the surface is desirable using either a "toothing" scraper, rough sandpaper or sand blasting.

There should be the minimum of delay in joining up the glued surfaces and 15 minutes is usually considered the maximum period which may safely elapse before clamping.

## Extending U. F. Glue With Rye Flour

The addition of rye flour to the adhesive renders it very economical in use and also greatly facilitates application. On the other hand, the strength of the joint is reduced in proportion to the degree of dilution with the extending agent and the water absorption of the joint is correspondingly increased. For high water resistant applications no extender can be safely employed and therefore its use is not general in the aircraft industry for the assembly of wood structures. It should, however, be remembered that a well balanced mixture of U. F. glue and rye flour is superior to a good casein glue.

There is no difficulty in mixing rye flour with U. F. glue provided the flour is added slowly whilst stirring. The mixing should preferably be carried out in an earthenware or enamel pan, but on no account must a copper or brass receptacle be employed. The addition of a small quantity of water may be necessary if the flour addition exceeds 20% by weight of the glue. Extended adhesive ready for immediate use should be free from lumps and easy to apply with either a brush or glue spreading machine. Flour is suitable for spreading by both hot and cold processes, and as much as 100 parts of rye flour to 100 parts of cement may be used although 70 parts of flour to 100 parts cement give the best all round results. (The use of inert organic material, such as calcium sulphate, Lenzine, is recommended where increased resistance to moisture is required. The extender is not, however, as economical in use as rye flour.)

## Pressing or Clamping

In actual practice the amount of pressure applied to the wood pieces does not specially matter provided that intimate contact between the wood surfaces is assured. In general the pressure should be enough to compress slightly the wood, i.e. 5 to 10%. It is recommended that in the case of plywood the pressure should vary from approximately 100 lbs. per sq. in. on basswood or spruce to 250 lbs. per sq. in. for maple or beech. Manufacturers stress the fact that the interval between the application of the adhesive and placing under pressure should be kept as short as possible and preferably not exceed 15 minutes. If once the adhesive dries out on the wood the resultant bond will be weak or spotty.

The Resinous Products and Chemical Co., Philadelphia, state that the higher pressures provide a margin of safety and should be employed where practical. Where head blocks are used, they should be approximately the same size as the sawn core block; otherwise deflection of "I" beams may result, giving insufficient pressure in the centre of the block. Clamps should be well tightened. When assembling hard wood structures to hard wood bases especial care must be taken to have enough pressure to obtain the proper contact. Bag pressure may be used, but the problem then becomes one of the mechanical construction of the pairs of forms to exert the pressure adequately. Pressure should be maintained for 8 hours at 70° F. which is adequate unless parts are under strain as in bent or curved plywood in which case the pressure needs to be continued 12 to 16 hours. In the manufacture of plywood by the hot pressing method the minimum time, depending on type of hardener employed, should be plus one minute for each millimetre (0.039 inch) wood, calculated to the deepest joint from the surface. The British concern, The Beetle Products Company, manufacturers of Beetle

Cement W. (Kaurit W.) give the following example of the pressing time of an assembly comprising

> Centre core of 20 mm (0.78 ins.)
> Cross bending of 3 mm (0.117 ins.)
> Face veneer of 0.8 mm (0.034 ins.)

which is as follows:

|  | *Hot Hardener Liquid* | *Hot Hardener 12* |
|---|---|---|
| Minimum time | 5 minutes | 8 minutes |
| Cross-bending 3 mm | 3 minutes | 3 minutes |
| Face veneer 0. 8 mm | 0.8 minutes | 0.8 minutes |
| Total time of pressing | 8.8 minutes | 11.8 minutes |
| Approximately | 9.0 minutes | 12.0 minutes |

## Time and Temperature

The above two factors are inter-related and dependent upon one another. Increase in temperature always means a diminution in the effective time required for bonding. A lowering of temperature is invariably accompanied by an increase in the time necessary to ensure satisfactory joining and below 70° F. the glueing operation becomes hazardous and uncertain. It is, therefore, always recommended that heat should be applied wherever possible so as to effect reasonably quick and very strong adhesion. The means of heating may be an electrically or steam heated platen such as would be used for plywood, local electric heating units, e.g. blankets, for special jobs, and overall increase in room temperature by use of air conditioning, steam radiators, electric fires or use of drying kilns. At a room temperature of 70–75°F., pressure, in the case of wood structures, should be maintained for 6 to 8 hours, after which the clamps may be removed and the material sawn, turned, or sanded.

The manufacturers of Uformite C. B. 500, the well known American urea-formaldehyde resin especially recommended for assembly work, say that even after clamps have been removed the bonds continue to strengthen, reaching maximum strength and waterproofness only after 48–72 hours. At higher temperatures clamping time can be materially reduced as well as the time required to reach maximum strength and waterproofness. For example, when clamped bonds are placed in drying kilns at 110–140°F. the clamping time can be reduced to 4 to 6 hours. In the case of thick lumber cores and large clamped bundles, where heat penetration is difficult it is sometimes advisable to preheat the sawn blocks or alternate members on sticks in the kiln. Cross bonds and lumber cores on which the adhesive is spread should not be preheated. Preheated stock must be removed from the kiln only long enough to permit assemblage and clamping and the entire bundle then returned promptly to the kiln.

It is necessary to remember that some U. F. glues are made specifically for high temperatures, i.e. 240–250°F. whereas others are developed for low temperatures, i.e. optimum of 70–80°F. Care must therefore be taken to ensure that the proper type of adhesive is chosen for each type of work such as plywood manufacture, improved wood and general assembly work. Once a particular kind of working condition is found successful, this should be standardized so as to ensure absolute uniformity of results. The clever use of heat in glueing operations can speed up the output and improve the strength of jointed materials.

## Ensuring Maximum Output of Glued Assemblies

The following factors are of great importance in relation to above:

1. Intimacy of contact between surfaces to be glued within reasonable limits of say 10–20/1000 ins.

2. Increase in temperature during setting within the limits prescribed for the particular glue employed.

3. Use, wherever possible, of combined glues, that is, one containing the hardener in solution. If the hardener is applied separately to the wood, there is some waste of valuable time.

4. Use of optimum low pressures to ensure perfect contact.

5. Use of minimum thickness coatings of adhesive consistent with the kind of glue, type and nature of application. (The joints must not be starved of glue through too rapid absorption.)

6. Physical condition of the wood also plays an important part and sanding or slight roughening of the surface greatly assists bonding.

7. Control of moisture contents of the woods to be bonded within the wide limits laid down, i.e. 0–25% so that there is some attempt to standardise the moisture content of wood assemblies put into work.

8. Use of an efficient plant and intelligent, but not necessarily skilled workers.

1. It was only the matter of a few years ago that a margin of 20/1000 ins. between wood members to be glued meant a considerable sacrifice of strength, owing to the wide difference that then existed between the strength of the gap joint and a similar joint made between closely fitting surfaces. Animal glue has until recently been able to give stronger gap joints than U. F. adhesives, mainly owing to the tendency of the latter, when present in the form of a relatively thick film, to craze, whilst hide glue or casein did not suffer so noticeably from this defect. Fortunately this defect has now been overcome and hardeners are available to ensure that thick films of urea-formaldehyde glues do not undergo these objectionable and weakening physical changes. To

make certain that gap joints attain maximum resistance to water it is recommended that the assembled structures should be kept at a room temperature of 70–75°F. for 2 to 3 weeks so that complete polymerisation of the resin may be assured. The importance of modern synthetic adhesives being able to bridge sizable gaps is of the utmost importance from the production angle as it enables some of the high precision wood finishing operations to be dispensed with and so permits a certain reduction of labor and time, thus speeding up output of many wood assemblies. Whilst latitude of finish can with most U. F. glues be permitted up to a maximum of 20/1000 ins. it is strongly advisable, however, that a somewhat lower limit say 10/1000 ins. be adopted. Irregularities within the prescribed limits in the intimacy of contact between wood surfaces to be glued might quite possibly reflect on the quality of goods turned out. In wartime, standardisation of quality is vital, particularly in the aircraft industry. Manufacturers should always make certain that the glues they use will safely compensate for gaps up to the limit of accuracy which they set themselves, whether 10 or 20/1000 ins.

2. Dealing with the second factor, making for better and more economical glueing, it is necessary to stress the great importance of temperature as controlling setting time. Although U. F. glues are classed as cold-setting glues, the minimum temperature should be 70°F. and it is recommended that wood assemblies, particularly those intended for aeronautical applications, should either have the glue joints warmed up by means of electric blankets or be placed in a kiln at a temperature of 90–95°F. where complete polymerisation can be assured. Economy in the use of heat in the glueing rooms means that setting time is slowed down and the joints take longer to gain maximum shear strength.

3. This is a rather obvious recommendation but one, nevertheless, which is not always fully appreciated.

Use of separate hardener solutions invariably means a slowing down of glueing operations as two operations are necessary instead of one. It is, however, necessary to bear in mind that where the hardener is used separately some discrimination can be shown as to the type to be employed, that is, if a rapid catalyst is needed, hot hardener, medium hardener, etc.

4. Optimum low pressure simply means that the pressure exercised is sufficient to ensure that contact between the members to be joined is closely intimate. All devices used to bring the glued surfaces together should be examined, this applies particularly to clamps, to see that the pressure is uniformly exercised over the entire area. Uneven pressure means uneven contact and gaping joints. In plywood manufacture this problem is non-existent as pressure can be applied to the degree required without any trouble. It is in the assembly of wood structures that irregularities of pressure are liable to occur.

5. Absorbent woods "mop up" the glue with such avidity that very often the coating is hardly sufficient to ensure effective bonding. When dealing with very open-structure woods the precaution should be taken to give two coatings of adhesive. It is essential that the film of glue should be adequate for the job in hand. Too little glue means a poor weak joint and, too much, that setting or curing takes a long time and full polymerisation with realisation of maximum strength may be delayed for several days.

6. It has been mentioned several times in this chapter that one of the aids to good glueing is the ability of the wood surface, by means of suitable roughening, to form a firm key for the glue coating. Whenever possible use should be made

of available tools for improving the glue adhering characteristics of the wood. Sanding and working with a "toothing" scraper are the best known and most reliable forms of
pre-glueing treatment.

7. When using U. F. glues the actual moisture content of
the wood does not matter as much as in the case of phenolic
glues and good results can be obtained up to and including
27% moisture content. What does matter is standardisation
of moisture content so as to ensure absolute uniformity of
results. This is particularly important in the case of wood
structures intended for aeronautical construction. Wide vari-
ances in the moisture content of wooden members must inevitably mean differences in sheer strength and the setting
up of certain stresses due to swelling or shrinking which may
induce failure of the joint. Uniformity of moisture content
should be aimed at by the manufacturer and the fact that U. F.
glue will join together wood containing a high percentage
of moisture does not mean that undue liberties can be safely
taken.

A new development of special interest in plywood manufacture is a foamed modified urea-formaldehyde glue which
in many respects combines the advantage of liquid and dry-
film glues with the added advantage of low cost. The idea
behind this process is that penetration of the glue into the
veneers is obviated; only a very thin film of glue is needed
to make good joints, and the amount of glue applied by any
ordinary means (glue spreaders or brushes) is in excess of
the optimum. By using the glue in about the same consistency as the lather produced from shaving soap, an extremely
thin uniform spread is obtained in terms of pounds of glue
per sq. ft., although the glue layer has an appreciable thickness. Actually, the volume of the glue is about doubled by
a special beater machine before it is poured into the glue
spreader. Under ordinary factory conditions, without taking

any special precautions it is possible to get a spread of 1.35 lbs. of glue per 100 sq. ft.

## Melamine Adhesives

An interesting account is given in Holztechnik, 1941, *21*, 208 of a new melamine resin used for wood assembly work in German aircraft factories. It is pointed out that resin-base glues, commonly in use at the moment, usually require the addition of hardeners, or curing by heat. To effect saving, fillers are sometimes added prior to use. Henckel, of Düsseldorf has marketed a melamine resin in the form of a drying powder, which, after mixing with cold water, is ready for use. Two qualities have been developed for purposes where resistance to water or moisture generally is required. The dry powder itself is very durable if stored away from damp and kept cool. After mixing with water the adhesive is stable for several days. In mixing, 10 to 15 minutes stirring with a mechanical stirrer is recommended, in order that lumpiness may be avoided; after this, the glue may be used immediately. A thin homogeneous coating is required, optimum figure being of the order of 200 to 250 gm. per sq. m. Hot pressing at 95–100° C. for a few minutes, dependent upon the thickness of the wood, is recommended. Optimum pressures for pine are 6 to 7 Kg. per sq. cm.; for beech, 15 to 23 Kg. per sq. cm. The new adhesive is particularly suitable, it is claimed, for furniture manufacture and for plywood flooring and composite boards.

Melamine hardeners for urea formaldehyde resin glues are now in common use in Great Britain to provide a glue bond that will withstand the boiling test.

# Chapter IV

# CELLULOSE ADHESIVES

## Cellulose Ester Cements

THE basic constituent of all these adhesives, namely the cellulose ester, can be modified a hundred different ways to produce cements with varying characteristics.

The standard formulation makes use of four main constituents, each one possessing the property of modifying the adhesive properties.

(1) The cellulose ester
(2) Resin
(3) Solvent
(4) Plasticiser

Cellulose nitrate, usually in the form of cinema film scrap, is the most widely used base and gives a stronger bond than the acetate. The mixed esters such as cellulose acetate butyrate and cellulose acetate propionate possess good adhesive properties and are superior to the straight acetate by reason of their better moisture resistance, increased solubility in a wider range of solvents, and the higher compatibility with more gums and resins resulting in improved adhesion.

The object of including resin in the cement formula must be considered under the following headings:

a. Reduces material costs of production, the resin being cheaper than the cellulose ester. This applies particularly to the mixed esters which are relatively expensive.
b. Increases the viscosity or body of the cement thus preventing "running" and "seeping" through joints.
c. Increases hardness of the film. Cellulose cements made without resin give a highly flexible and soft film, which, although useful for certain applications, is a disadvantage for others.
d. Resin increases the lustre and bonding properties of the straight cellulose cement.

In the writer's opinion the most effective resin for use in making high grade commercial cellulose adhesives is a mixture of ester gum and coumarone resin as recommended by Dulac "Colles à Froid Industrielles." Usually the resin employed is a mixture of wood rosin, ester gum, Bakelite 3180, etc.

The following resins are compatible with the mixed esters:
Wood rosin "N"
Santolite MHP
Vinsol
Bakelite 3180
Rezyl 14
Gelva 2½
Aroclor 1254
Ester gum
Durez 550
Damar
Gum Elemi

The proportions of resins recommended as compatible by Tennessee Eastman Corp., manufacturers of cellulose acetate butyrate and cellulose acetate propionate, are:

1. 20% resin for all types of mixed resin containing 15% dibutyl phthalate as plasticizer.

2. 40% resin (except Rezyl 14 and damar) for mixed resin (12–15% acetyl content, <0.5% propionyl content and 35–38% butyryl content).

3. 60% resin (all except Rezyl 14 and damar) for mixed ester as in (2).

4. 40% resin (all except ester gum, damar and gum Elemi) for mixed resin (30½–33% acetyl content; <0.5% propionyl content; 14–17% butyryl content) containing the same amount of plasticizer as in (1).

5. 60% resin (all except ester gum, damar and gum Elemi) for the mixed ester as in (4).

6. 40% resin (all except wood rosin "N," ester gum, damar, gum Elemi) for mixed ester (14–17% acetyl content; 30–33% propionyl content; <0.5% butyryl content).

7. 60% resin (all except wood rosin "N," ester gum, damar, gum Elemi) for the mixed ester as in (6).

An average of 60 to 65% resin on the weight of ester will give very good results in the case of ester gum, coumarone, Gelva mixtures, but it is possible to increase the resin above this range to 75% of the weight of cellulose ester without any serious sacrifice of adhesive properties. Blended resin mixtures are preferable to straight additions of a single resin and with the former it is usually possible to cheapen production by use of such cheap additions as wood rosin.

## Solvent

Choice of solvent influences to a considerable degree the usefulness of the made-up cement. The solvent should be blended so that it evaporates without causing the film of adhesive to blush. In considering the types of solvents which may safely be employed in mixture form, the following main factors have to be carefully reviewed:

(a) Ability of the solvent to evaporate with sufficient speed to enable bonding to be effected rapidly.

(b) Ability of the solvent, either single or mixture, to resist blushing of film during drying.

(c) The mixture of solvent and diluent chosen should be able to increase the viscosity of the solution to the desired extent without any tendency to promote too extensive gelatinization or precipitation of the ester.

(d) The solvent (this is taken to include diluent) should be economic in use.

(e) The solvent must be reasonably safe to handle, i.e. not highly toxic or highly inflammable.

The following solvents and diluents are recommended for the cellulose esters:

| | *Solvent* | *Diluent* |
|---|---|---|
| Cellulose Nitrate | Ethyl acetate | Benzene |
| | Butyl acetate | Toluene |

One of the most useful solvent mixtures for cellulose nitrate is the azeotropic mixture suggested by Dulac, namely 68% benzene and 32% of 95% denatured alcohol or 32% toluene and 68% of 95% industrial alcohol. These two mixtures swell the ester to such an extent that it only requires a very small percentage of ethyl acetate or acetone, etc., to form the solution.

| | *Solvent* | *Diluent* |
|---|---|---|
| Cellulose Acetate | Acetone | Benzene |
| | Methyl acetate | |
| | Ethyl acetate | |

Cellulose Mixed Esters.
    (Med. Viscosity)

| Solvent | Diluent |
|---|---|
| Acetone | Benzene-alcohol |
| Methyl ethyl ketone | mixtures |
| Diacetone alcohol | Toluene-alcohol |
| 1, 4 Dioxane | mixtures |
| Methyl acetate, 88% | |
| Butyl acetate | |
| Cellosolve acetate | |
| Methyl cellosolve acetate | |
| Ethyl lactate | |
| Ethylene dichloride | |
| Mixtures 80% Ethylene dichloride | |
| 20% Ethyl alcohol | |

## Plasticizer

The function of the plasticizer is of the utmost importance as it prevents the plastic, i.e. the cellulose ester, from drying out hard, brittle and therefore unable to effect lasting bonds, in other words, the plasticizer gives to the ester the necessary degree of plasticity or flexibility.

A good plasticizer must be a product of low vapor pressure at N. T. P., chemically stable in contact with water, a solvent for the product to be plasticized and possess lubricating properties, resistance to light, etc. Generally speaking camphor and the phthalates, e.g. dibutyl phthalate, etc., are the best known plasticizers, but for adhesive purposes many other cheaper materials may be used, particularly castor oil and rape oil, in conjunction with cellulose nitrate.

The range of plasticizers is an exceedingly wide one and new materials are constantly being introduced to the trade. A much smaller quantity of plasticizer is required with cellulose mixed esters than with cellulose acetate. In general, the higher the butyryl or propionyl content the less plasticizer is required and the greater is the compatibility with the various plasticizers. Tennessee Eastman Kodak Corporation gives the list below of plasticizers that have proved useful with mixed esters :

Butyl phthalyl butyl glycollate
Ethyl phthalyl ethyl glycollate
Methyl phthalyl ethyl glycollate
Diamyl phthalate
Dibutyl phthalate
Dipropyl phthalate
Diethyl phthalate
Dimethyl phthalate
Dibutoxy ethyl phthalate
Dimethoxy ethyl phthalate
Tributyl phosphate
Tricresyl phosphate
Triphenyl phosphate
Dibutyl sebacate
Diethyl sebacate
Butyl stearate
Butyl tartrate

Many industrial cements are made with cinema scrap, which contains camphor as the plasticizer, and these give good results, although it is not generally possible to produce such a "heavy" adhesive as is practical when using collodion quality cellulose nitrate and added plasticizers.

## Industrial Adhesives from Cellulose Scrap

A. Bresser, "Synthetic and Applied Finishes," May, 1935, gives several interesting recipes for cleaned scrap cements.

*No. 1.*

| | |
|---|---|
| Celluloid | 20 parts by weight |
| Acetone | 60 parts by weight |
| Copal | 5 parts by weight |
| Rosin | 5 parts by weight |
| White lead | 1 part by weight |

## No. 2.

| | |
|---|---|
| Scrap film (cleaned) | 14 parts |
| Ethyl acetanilide | 2 parts |
| Castor oil | 2 parts |
| Tricresyl phosphate | 3 parts |
| Ethyl acetate | 13 parts |
| Methyl acetate | 13 parts |
| Acetone | 21 parts |
| Benzine | 6 parts |
| Starch | 20 parts |

Dulac mentions the following film scrap cements:

## No. 3. (cheap)

| | Parts | |
|---|---|---|
| Benzene | 580 | |
| Denatured alcohol 95% | 265 | Soak for 12 hours. |
| Castor oil | 12 | |
| Rosin | 30 | |
| Film scrap | 100 | |
| Ethyl acetate | 210 | Add and mix until dissolved. |

## No. 4. (improved)

| | Parts | |
|---|---|---|
| Benzene | 550 | |
| Denatured alcohol 95% | 250 | |
| Butyl alcohol | 8 | Soak for 12 hours. |
| Castor oil | 12 | |
| Ester gum | 20 | |
| Coumarone resin | 10 | |
| Film scrap | 100 | |
| Ethyl acetate | 200 | Add and mix until dissolved. |

The writer considers that the following two recipes show promise although they may be a little more expensive than those suggested by Dulac.

### No. 5.

| | Parts | |
|---|---|---|
| Benzene and alcohol mixture (80% benzene and 20% alcohol) | 600 | |
| Butyl alcohol | 10 | Soak for 12 hours. |
| Gelva 2½ | 35 | |
| Araclor 1254 | 5 | |
| Film scrap | 120 | |
| Castor oil | 5 | |
| Ethyl acetate | 50 | |
| Cellosolve acetate | 150 | |

### No. 6.

| | Parts | |
|---|---|---|
| Benzene and alcohol mixture (as in 5) | 500 | |
| Butyl alcohol | 10 | Soak for 12 hours. |
| Bakelite 3180 | 10 | |
| Vinsol | 20 | |
| Ester gum | 10 | |
| Castor oil | 5 | |
| Ethyl acetate | 50 | |
| Cellosolve acetate | 150 | |

## Nitro-Cotton Cements

A good workable cellulose adhesive can be produced quite simply. U. S. Pat. No. 1,969,477 describes a typical cement comprising

4–5 parts nitro-cellulose
1 part plasticizer
100 parts liquid mixture of solvents
5 parts water.

Another U. S. Patent, No. 2,046,925 gives a high castor oil content formula, namely, a mixture of cellulose nitrate with 65.3 to 71.5 vol. % castor oil dissolved in a suitable solvent, e.g., butyl acetate 25%, butyl alcohol 10%, ethyl acetate 10%, ethyl alcohol 5%, toluene 50%. This type of adhesive is claimed to be particularly useful when bonding smooth surfaces.

Serviceable cements may be obtained by blending rubber in the form of crepe latex or chlorinated rubber with nitro-cellulose, the latter addition decreases the drying time and improves chemical resistance. A. Bresser, "Cellulose Ester Adhesives, Synthetic and Applied Finishes," May, 1935, gives some data about these rubber modified cements.

Sol. 1. 12.8 Kg. alcohol damp nitro-cotton in 12.0 Kg. methyl acetate

Sol. 2. 25.0 Kg. first crepe latex dissolved in 72 Kg. benzole.

The two solutions are mixed and thinned to the required viscosity.

Straight forward nitro-cellulose cements can be made by dissolving 15 parts nitro-cotton, 5 parts camphor and 1 part tricresyl phosphate in 60 parts acetone and 20 parts ethyl acetate, 10 parts resin and filler such as aluminum powder, starch, etc.

Of considerable interest are the special nitro-cellulose cements produced to meet new conditions of manufacture and solve tricky industrial problems. Such a one is mentioned in Brit. Pat. No. 500, 949. This is a heat-activated adhesive, which comprises a thermo-plastic (modified alkyd) resin, a cellulose derivative (nitrate), a solvent or solvent mixture and 1–10% on the total solids of a finely dispersed wax or wax-like substance, e.g. carnauba wax, metallic stearates, chlorinated paraffin wax, which is incompatible with the composition at room temperature and thus renders the deposited film non-adhesive so that, e.g. treated paper can be rolled and stored without premature adhesion. At working temperature the wax melts or dissolves in the film which becomes adhesive.

Du Pont, U. S. Pats. Nos. 2,092,050 and 2,092,084, describe a cellulose nitrate adhesive which can be applied to at least one of the surfaces to be joined and allowed to harden, later it is softened by applying a volatile liquid activator consisting of a solvent mixture, 90% propylene oxide containing 0.5 to 2% non-volatile plasticizer, and 10% ethyl acetate and methyl alcohol, and the surfaces united under pressure.

Another patented heat-activated adhesive that is non-tacky at ordinary temperatures offers a new solution to the problem of stacking adhesive coated materials without having them stuck together. Typical composition is:

| | | |
|---|---|---|
| Cellulose nitrate | 7.5 | parts by weight |
| Alcohol | 9.2 | parts by weight |
| Toluol | 27.0 | parts by weight |
| Butyl phthalate | 5.9 | parts by weight |
| Ethyl acetate | 29.4 | parts by weight |
| Alkyd resin | 2.7 | parts by weight |
| Synthetic resin | 12.3 | parts by weight |
| Solvent naphtha | 4.5 | parts by weight |

To increase the toughness and reduce the inflammability of pyroxylin cements the addition of ethyl cellulose is recommended. The following formula is suggested:

|                   | Parts |                              |
|-------------------|-------|------------------------------|
| Cellulose nitrate | 10    |                              |
| Ethyl cellulose   | 5     |                              |
| Castor oil        | 10    |                              |
| Alkyd resin       | 2     | Allow to soak for 12 hours.  |
| Benzine           | 25    |                              |
| Alcohol           | 35    |                              |
| Acetone           | 20    |                              |
| Ethyl acetate     | 25    | Add and mix thoroughly.      |

Ethyl cellulose is freely soluble in ethyl alcohol, amyl alcohol, benzyl alcohol, also carbon tetrachloride, methylene chloride, etc.

Acrylic resins, particularly the co-polymers, e.g. the Acryloids produced by the Resinous Products and Chemical Co., may be used in conjunction with nitro-cellulose and ethyl cellulose to increase adhesive properties. These acrylic resins may be plasticized with the same materials as the cellulose esters and ethers and are compatible with most of the common resins.

## Cellulose Acetate Cements

These are not so useful as the nitro-cellulose cements, but the following suggestion is made regarding their production.

|                      | Parts |                              |
|----------------------|-------|------------------------------|
| Cellulose acetate    | 10    |                              |
| Tricresyl phosphate  | 5     |                              |
| Alkyd resin          | 2     | If acetate scrap is used the |
| Ethyl acetate        | 25    | plasticizer can be cut down  |
| Methyl alcohol       | 10    | to 2 parts.                  |
| Benzine              | 15    |                              |
| Methyl acetate       | 25    |                              |
| Filler               | 15    |                              |

Sheets of cellulose acetate can be cemented together to make strong joints by use of the following simple solvent solution.

Benzene 200 ccs.
Acetone 4½ litres

Method of application recommended is:

Clean the surfaces to be bonded together by wiping them with a rag moistened with acetone. Allow to dry and then apply a coating of the jointing cement or plain solvent solution. When the cellulose acetate surface has dried to a slightly tacky condition apply a further coating and leave until really tacky. Place the surfaces in contact with each other and apply gentle pressure until a strong bond is effected.

In the manufacture of so-called safety or compound glass the interlayer of cellulose acetate, which may consist of 1 to 3 layers of acetate, two of which are fairly heavily plasticized, is immersed in a special solvent solution, e.g. mixture of ethyl lactate or triacetin. The sandwich, that is the softened interlayer laid loosely between the glass sheets, is then passed through a roller to give adhesion and united by heat and pressure.

## Cellulose Mixed Ester Cements

As explained previously these comparatively new adhesives are of considerable interest and show promise for a variety of industrial applications. The information given below is a working suggestion and may be adapted to the necessary requirements.

| | |
|---|---|
| Cellulose acetate propionate | 10 parts |
| Tributyl phthalate | 2 parts |
| Butyl stearate | 1 part |
| Bakelite 3180 | 10 parts |

| Santolite | 20 parts |
| Toluene methyl alcohol mixture | |
| (equal parts) | 30 parts |
| Ethyl acetate | 20 parts |
| Butyl alcohol | 3 parts |
| Cellosolve acetate | 15 parts |

Similar cements can be made using the acetate butyrate.

CELLULOSE ETHER CEMENTS

## Ethyl Cellulose

Straight ethyl cellulose cements and ethyl modified adhesives are now being employed for bonding cloth, paper, foil, etc. and also as shoe cements. They offer advantages over certain other cellulose thermo-plastic adhesives by reason of their great toughness, waterproofness and heat sealing properties. Where high flexibility and elasticity of film are required ethyl cellulose should be used either alone or as an important ingredient of the recipe.

Common plasticizers for ethyl cellulose are castor oil, butyl stearate, dibutyl tartrate, tricresyl phosphate, etc. Resins such as dewaxed dammar, shellac white, ester gum and wood rosin, are all compatible with ethyl cellulose. Common solvents are the alcohols, carbon tetrachloride, methylene chloride, toluene 80% and alcohol 20% mixture, benzol 80% and methanol 20%, Solvesso, and Solvesso and alcohol mixtures.

Excellent cements can be made by use of the following type of formula:

1 part ethyl cellulose
0.5–5 parts resin, wax, oil or plasticizer
Solvent to give desired viscosity

An early stage in the manufacture of cellulose esters. The operations consist of dumping cotton linters into this specially built acetylator where they are mixed with a solution of acetic anhydride and acetic acid. (*Courtesy of Tennessee Eastman Corp., Kingsport, Tennessee*)

Tipping out cellulose acetate from the acetylator. The acetate is then hydrolized in huge storage jars, plunged into cold water where it precipitates into flake form. After being washed free of acid and dried it is ready for commercial use.

Ethyl cellulose is available in several viscosity types and is more economical in use than cellulose nitrate or other esters owing to its low density, 1.14 at 25° C., compared to 1.37 for cellulose acetate and 1.65 for nitrocellulose. Hercules Powder Co. state that one pound of ethyl cellulose will cover as much surface as 1.20 lbs. of cellulose acetate, or as much as 1.45 lbs. of nitro-cellulose with the same film thickness.

The following suggestions are made for ethyl cellulose cements:

| | |
|---|---|
| Ethyl cellulose | 10 parts |
| Ester gum | 2 parts |
| Aroclor 5460 | 2 parts |
| Castor oil (raw) | 2 parts |
| Industrial alcohol | 10 parts |
| Toluol and alcohol mixture | 60 parts |

*Note*: The solvent must be varied to meet requirements of viscosity.

| | |
|---|---|
| Ethyl cellulose | 10 parts |
| Bakelite B. R. 820 | 4 parts |
| Wood rosin | 5 parts |
| Ester gum | 2 parts |
| Aroclor No. 1260 | 5 parts |

Solvent to meet requirements of viscosity.

The Aroclors are very compatible with ethyl cellulose, the liquids imparting flexibility and the resinous products hardness. From the adhesive standpoint the liquid Aroclors are the most useful and Aroclor 1260 is specially recommended.

### Benzyl Cellulose

This ether is fairly well known in the lacquer field but so far not much used for adhesives. It is more expensive than ethyl cellulose and does not give such a tough film. Comparative tensile strength data on dry films of various cellulose derivatives is given by Hercules Powder Company:

|  | Breaking Strength Kg/Sq. Cm | Elongation % |
|---|---|---|
| Ethyl Cellulose | 450–700 | 15–25 |
| Benzyl Cellulose | 350–375 | 18–20 |
| Nitro Cellulose | 350–700 | 4–6 |
| Cellulose Acetate | 425–475 | 6–10 |

The outstanding property of benzyl cellulose film is its resistance to moisture and where the adhesive is required to have a very low moisture absorption benzyl cellulose should be employed. The recipe may be similar to that suggested for ethyl cellulose.

Heat-sealing adhesives for use in sealing food packs can be made of ethyl or benzyl cellulose, or mixtures of these with cellulose esters.

Cellulose ethers and esters are used in the manufacture of thermo-adhesive fabric for use as a lining for collars, cuffs, shirt fronts and the like. The fabric is coated with a composition containing the cellulose derivative, plasticizer and solvent. Brit. Pat. No. 461,847 gives a suitable composition as 40% cellulose acetate and 60% ethyl-o-benzoyl benzoate.

### Methyl Cellulose

This compound can be mixed with water to give a workable size solution. This is suitable as an adhesive for use in book-binding, also for textile finishing and dressing agents and colour binding agents.

The great advantage of a size made with methyl cellulose over natural sizes made with animal glues, starch, etc., is that the former does not deteriorate through putrefaction or mold deposits whereas, of course, all sizes made with natural products are affected very quickly on exposure to the atmosphere.

# CHAPTER V

# POLYVINYL CEMENTS

## Gelvas and Alvars

POLYVINYL acetate and chloride, also the butyrate, or mixtures of these, are now finding very important applications as adhesives owing to their remarkable power of adhesion to a variety of porous and non-porous materials, including wood, metal, plastics, ceramics, cloth, felt, leather and various compositions such as Pliofilm, Cellophane, celluloid, mica, stone, etc. For joining certain molded or laminated plastic structures polyvinyl cements, which can be neatly applied and are air-drying, offer signal advantages over the normal baking phenolic resins. The Vidal process for the production of large laminated wood units for aircraft construction makes use of polyvinyl cement as well as phenolic resin glue. At present the polyvinyl adhesives find their best known use in the manufacture of safety glass for which they are well fitted, not only on account of the high strength of bond, but also because, as the properly compounded vinyl cement has approximately the same refractive index as glass, there is no indication of the presence of the bonding agent or line of demarcation, and vision is in no way impaired.

The two best known polyvinyl adhesives on the market are the range of materials known as Gelvas and Alvars. These are vinyl resin materials produced by Shawinigan Chemicals Ltd., Quebec, Canada. It is of interest to note that the Gelvas and Alvars were initially produced as by-products from the synthesis of acetic anyhdride from acetic acid and acetylene and intensive research was carried out for several years before they were accepted by the trade.

The Gelvas are polyvinyl acetates which are available in forms, differing in molecular weight and viscosity. The number associated with the term Gelvar or Formvar, etc., refers to the viscosity in centipoises determined at 20° C. of a benzene solution containing 86 grams of Gelvar per litre. The Formvars are acetates produced by the partial hydrolysis of a Gelvar and subsequent reaction with formaldehyde. Butvars are similar only butyraldehyde is substituted for formaldehyde. Alvars are produced from Gelvas by reaction of the hydrolysis product with acetaldehyde. It will thus be appreciated that the Gelvas are vinyl "acetates" and the Formvars, Butvars, etc., "acetals."

Gelvas are of the greatest interest as adhesives and the following is the standard range of viscosities, 1.5, 2.5, 7, 15, 25, 45 and 60 cp. Choice of any particular grade depends entirely upon the nature of the application.

E. E. Halls, "Plastics," April 1941, gives the following useful data about Gelvas. He claims that one of the outstanding characteristics of the range is their remarkable power of adhesion to porous and non-porous surfaces. The strength of a bond on a straight pull where various polished metals and glass were bonded without pressure was in excess of 1 ton per sq. in. (1.5 Kg per sq. mm.). Hall states that bonds have actually been made so strong that conchoidal pieces were pulled out of  plate glass without breaking the bond to a metal plug.

The data given below is abstracted from Hall's excellent survey:

*Physical Constants of the Gelvas*

| | |
|---|---|
| Specific Gravity at 20° C. ................... | 1.19 |
| Refractive Index $n_D^{20}$ ....................... | 1.467 |
| Dielectric Strength, volt/mil. ................ | 1,000 |
| Dielectric Constant at 30° C. ............... | 2.7 |
| Coefficient Linear Expansion ................ | 0.000086 |
| Water Absorption (A. S. T. M.) .......... | 2.0 |
| Acid Value ................................. | Nil |

*Softening Point (Kraemer and Sarnov), Tensile Strength and Viscosity*

| Gelva Grade | Soft. Pt., ° C. | Tensile Strength, lbs. per sq. in. | Viscosity Weight % Concentration of Toluene Solution at 2.5 'poises. |
|---|---|---|---|
| 1.5 | 65 | .... | 55 |
| 2.5 | 81 | .... | 45 |
| 7 | 106 | .... | 32 |
| 15 | 131 | 5,000 | 25 |
| 25 | 151 | 5,000 | 20 |
| 45 | 183 | 5,000 | 17 |
| 60 | 196 | 5,000 | 14 |

The polyvinyl range of adhesives in their various viscosities are soluble in a number of solvents, such as ketones, benzene, toluene, methylated spirits, chlorinated hydrocarbons and esters. Suitable plasticizers are: triethylene glycol hexoate, tributyl phosphate, dimethyl cellosolve phthalate, dibutyl phthalate, dibutyl tartrate. Hall states that the addition of DoWP2 and DoWP4, non-plasticizing diluents, improve the water resistance of the Gelvar formulae.

The three general methods of employing these adhesives are:

(a) to apply the cement, allow to dry, subsequently to moisten with solvent and apply pressure

(b) to apply the cement, bring the two surfaces in contact and apply pressure

(c) to apply the cement, allow to dry, subsequently to
heat the resin and render thermo-plastic and able
to effect a joint between the two surfaces.

The first method gives the strongest joint, but for certain
applications (b) may be necessary. The method (c) is extensively used for labelling and sealing in the food industry
and is very suitable for sealing "Cellophane" packs.

Hall's "Plastics," June, 1942, gives some interesting data
concerning the properties of polyvinyl acetate adhesives as
compared with standard air-drying phenolic resin rubber cement. The tests were carried out by fixing the materials to

## LAP JOINTS IN VARIOUS MATERIALS USING AIR-DRYING PHENOLIC RESIN CEMENT AND AIR-DRYING POLYVINYL ACETATE ADHESIVES.

| Combination No. | Materials Lapped | Air-Drying Phenolic Resin Rubber Cement No. 1 | Air-Drying Polyvinyl Acetate Cement No. 2 | Air-Drying Polyvinyl Acetate Cement No. 3 |
|---|---|---|---|---|
| 1. | Phenolic laminated/ paper | Good | Good | Poor |
| 2. | Phenolic laminated/ phenolic laminated | Rather poor | Good | Very poor |
| 3. | Plywood/ plywood | Very good | Excellent | Poor |
| 4. | Phenolic laminated/ plywood | Good | Fairly good | Very poor |
| 5. | Phenolic laminated/ brass | Rather poor | Poor. Brass corroded to green copper compounds. | Very poor |
| 6. | Brass/ plywood | Poor | Poor | Poor |
| 7. | Soft rubber/ plywood | Poor | Poor | Poor |
| 8. | Bituminized cement asbestos board/ bituminized cement asbestos board | Very poor | Very poor | Very poor |

be bonded together by means of the adhesive in lap fashion. The phenolic resin rubber cement has a composition of 15% total solids and 85.0% volatile spirit and an acid value, expressed in terms of mgms. KOH per gr. of resinous base. Polyvinyl acetate cement No 2 consisted of 29.5% solids and 70.5% solvent, acid value 15.5. Polyvinyl acetate cement No 3, 22.5% total solids and 77.5 solvent with the low acid value of 1.3.

The writer considers that the following points should be borne in mind when using polyvinyl resin adhesives.

1. Choose a suitable viscosity resin so that the adhesive is best suited for the surfaces to be bonded. Low viscosity Gelva is not so suitable for a porous surface as a moderately high one owing to the inevitable loss of resin through penetration.

2. Use ketones as solvents and hydrocarbons as diluents. Ethers, esters and alcohols tend to induce gel formation or precipitation.

3. To enable the resin solution to give a bond of great toughness and body the use of nitro-cellulose is recommended.

4. Increase in stability of the film can be afforded by use of various additions, e.g. a British Patent claims that phenol salicylate when milled with the resin prevents premature embrittling and discoloring through the action of light. The use of stearates is stated to improve the heat stability of the adhesive. Chlorinated rubber is a very useful addition for vinyl acetate adhesives to increase heat stability. DOWP2 and DOWP4 are claimed to increase the water-resistance of the cements.

5. Plasticizers should be used very sparingly as they tend to lower the adhesive properties of the resin if

employed to the same extent as is necessary in the case of the cellulose esters.

6. It is generally unnecessary to incorporate natural resins in the cement, but if resin is to be employed it is often advisable that it should be mixed with the polyvinyl resin (acetate) in a kneading machine at 120–250° F. for an hour or so. Brit. Pat. No. 510,826 mentions a thermoplastic adhesive produced by mixing 25–40% dammar gum with 60–75% polyvinyl acetate. (The use of resin usually cheapens the adhesive.)

Acrylic resins can usefully be employed with polyvinyl acetates. Brit. Pat. No. 461,684 describes a compound glass comprising external glass sheets supported by a flexible intermediate layer approximately 70% of the thickness of the thicker glass sheet and made by mixing polymerized vinyl acetate and polymerized acrylic acid ester with 7–20% of a softening agent, heating and extending to form a sheet.

One of the best known inter-layers for laminated safety glass is the Du Pont material "Butacite" polyvinyl acetal plastic which is "sandwiched" between two sheets of plate glass. This plastic excels in clarity and color and is highly resistant to the deteriorating influences of heat, light and moisture. Its unusual ability to stretch and yield under impact tends to lessen the blow to persons thrown against windows or windshields in the case of accidents.

## Polyvinyl Chloride

Polyvinyl chloride (Korolac, a solution of Koroseal made by B. F. Goodrich Co.) offers interesting possibilities as an adhesive for special applications where high chemical resistance or good dielectric properties are needed. The remarkable corrosion resistance of Koroseal arises from the chemical stability of gamma polyvinyl chloride, which, in turn, results from its absence of olefinic unsaturation and its high chlorine content. Early samples of Koroseal have retained their physical properties for 12 years without appreciable change. Accelerated ageing tests in the Bierer bomb and Geer oven produce practically no change in tensile strength and elongation.

## Polyvinyl Alcohol

This product is a white, odorless powder, specific gravity 0.4–0.6, soluble in water at 70°C. and also glycerin and glycol. Aqueous solutions are exceedingly stable and are recommended as binding agents in the food industry. The dried film is clear, colorless, tough, impermeable to gases, resistant to fats and many solvents.

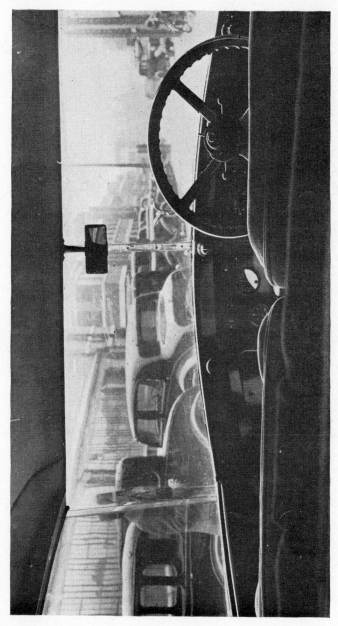

This wide expanse of safety glass windowscreen was produced with the aid of polyvinyl resin adhesives notable for great adhesion to smooth surfaces and ability to resist the darkening effect of indefinite exposure to light.

Transparent wrappings need to be sealed effectively. Synthetic adhesives such as polyvinyl and cellulose esters are most commonly employed for this purpose and may be modified to meet all practical requirements of modern packaging machinery.

62

CHAPTER VI

# ACRYLIC RESIN CEMENTS

THE polymers of acrylic acid derivatives are now being extensively employed as impermeable coatings for a variety of materials and as adhesives for thermo-plastics, textiles, leather, "Cellophane," metal foils, wood, rubber, etc. Of primary interest are the acrylic ester resins known as Acryloid and Acrysol produced by The Resinous Products and Chemical Co. These materials are manufactured and sold under license of the Röhm and Haas Co., who own the principal patents in this field. The characteristics of the polymers depend to a large extent upon the chemical constitution of the monomeric forms, although the conditions, under which the polymerization is effected, also have a considerable influence. Polymethyl acrylate is a colorless, transparent substance. At ordinary temperatures a film of it is tough, pliable, and so elastic as to be capable of being stretched 1,000% before a break occurs. Polyethyl acrylate is softer and even more elastic than the methyl ester, but not quite so tough. The polymer of n-butyl acrylate is so soft that at ordinary temperatures it remains rather tacky to the touch. In general, the softness of the polymers increases as the length of the alcohol chain increases.

Physical mixtures of different polymers do not exhibit the desirable combinations of properties expected, frequently due to surprising incompatibilities. However, this difficulty may be overcome and additional advantages may be obtained by mixing the monomeric forms in desirable proportions before polymerization is effected.

Acryloids are solutions of such copolymers designed to yield the most advantageous combination of properties in a convenient range of relative hardness, elasticity, and solubility. They are distinguished from other resins by their colorless transparency, adhesive qualities, great elasticity and chemical resistance. Because of their remarkable stability to the destructive effects of heat and light, their durability is excellent. Clear films transmit a substantial portion of light in the ultraviolet portion of the spectrum. They have an index of refraction of approx. 1.49 and specific gravity of approx. 1.15.

The acrylic resin films dry at ordinary temperatures by solvent evaporation, much like nitro-cellulose lacquers. It is very desirable, however, to bake the films at moderate temperature to obtain the best results in gloss, adhesion and hardness. Acryloid coatings are recommended for use where their unusual combination of properties may be used to the best advantage. This combination includes water-white color, color stability, unusual adhesion, flexibility, electrical resistance, and resistance to ozone, mineral and animal oils, and dilute acids and alkalies.

Acrysols are similar polymers produced in aqueous emulsion. They are miscible with letex and find applications where it is advantageous to use emulsions in water rather than organic solutions, as in base coatings on leather, artificial leather, textiles, paper and rubber.

The following are the main types of acrylic resins for use as adhesives.

## Acryloid A-10

This grade, which is supplied as a 30% solution in cellulose acetate, is recommended for the thermo-plastic bonding of transparent or flexible materials or especially smooth surfaces. The resin is soluble in butyl acetate, ethyl acetate, toluol, tetralin, etc., and is compatible with nitro-cellulose and a number of plasticizers, e.g. dibutyl phthalate, dibutyl sebacate, etc. The viscosity of the supplied solution is 53–58 sec. (50 gm. wt) Stormer 30° C.; Gardner Holdt 25° C. U–W. Specific gravity of the film (25° C.) is 1.19 and refractive index 1–490. The softening temperature is approximately 110° C., water absorption nil, electrical resistance $10^{10}$ ohms/cm$^3$, dielectric strength 800 V/mil, power factor at 1,000 cycles 5.8 and dielectric constant at 1,000 cycles 3.4.

For application of a clear coating by brushing it is as well to thin to 15% solids with a higher boiling solvent such as butyl acetate or cellosolve acetate. Although the straight solution of resin is quite capable of bonding many surfaces it is usually considered advisable to modify the resin with 15–20% plasticizer, such as a mixture of dibutyl sebacate and dibutyl phthalate, and 15–20% cellulose nitrate.

## Acryloid C-10

This is well adapted to the coating of flexible materials, and is especially useful to secure excellent adhesion to metal. It is recommended as a thermoplastic adhesive where resistance to hot laundering conditions is not necessary. The resin is supplied as a 20% solution in ethyl acetate. The film produced is perfectly clear, colorless, extremely elastic and slightly tacky at ordinary temperatures.

The supplied solution has a viscosity (Stormer, 30° C. approx.) 55–65 Sec. (500 gm. wt.) and Gardner-Holdt 25° C. Za–Z5. The film has a specific gravity of 1.22, refractive index 1.481, softening temperature 10–25° C., a tensile strength (A. S. T. M.) of 1,750 lbs./sq. in. and 625% elongation, water absorption (after 48 hours immersion) 1.99% and electrical properties practically the same as A-10.

A typical formulation for base coat on fabrics is given by the Resinous Products and Chemical Co.

| | |
|---|---|
| Acryloid C-10 (20%) | 200 parts |
| ½ Second Nitrocellulose 70% | 43 parts |
| Dibutyl sebacate or dibutyl phthalate | 30 parts |

Reduce to consistency required with ethyl acetate or other solvents.

## Acrysol C-9

This is supplied as a 25% dispersion in water. The dispersion has approximately the viscosity of water itself. When flowed out on a glass plate and dried, the film is slightly tacky, and very slightly opaque. It is compatible with latex and can be readily sprayed alone or in combination with latex. It is particularly adapted for application to rubber or rubberized surfaces where the adhesion is difficult. It is used alone or in combination with latex as a base coat over which a subsequent coating of Acryloid B-7 or Acryloid C-10 plus nitrocellulose is applied. Freezing must be avoided, as it destroys the Acrysol dispersion.

## Main Advantages of Acrylic Resin Adhesives

1. Colorless, transparent bonds.
2. Elasticity and flexibility permit their use where the bonded assemblies are subject to flexure and elongation.
3. Excellent electrical properties and therefore suitability for all kinds of assembly work in the electrical industries.
4. Freedom from bacterial and fungus deterioration.
5. Compatibility with nitro-cellulose and plasticizers so that their physical properties may be suitably modified.

Synthetic adhesives, odorless, tasteless and unaffected by solvents, weak acids, alkalies, moisture, etc., are needed to cement liners to bottle and jar closures. Acrylic resins are particularly suitable for this application although others are extensively employed.

CHAPTER VII

# CHLORINATED RUBBER AND SYNTHETIC RUBBER CEMENTS

## Chlorinated Rubber

THIS material is now finding a number of applications as an adhesive or for modifying other adhesives. Chlorinated rubber is available as a white granular powder having a specific gravity of 1.64. It is usually manufactured in several different viscosities, e.g. Hercules chlorinated rubber is produced in 5 cp, 10 cp, 20 cp, 125 cp, 1,000 cp (all viscosities determined in a 20% solution in toluol at 25° C.). The non-plasticized clear film has a strength (breaking load) of 300–400 kg/cm (dry) and 90% of dry strength (wet) ; modulus of elasticity, lb./in. 1.47 x 10 and flexibility, Schopper folds

| | |
|---|---|
| 5 and 10 cp | 0 |
| 20 cp | 0.5–1.5 |
| 125 cp | 3–6 |
| 1,000 cp | 8.15 |

Chlorinated rubber is non-inflammable, stable at 125° C. and decomposes at 135–150° C. It is freely soluble in benzene, toluene, xylene, Hi-flash solvent naphtha, carbon tetrachloride, ethylene dichloride, ethyl acetate (85 C E), butyl acetate, octyl acetate, methyl ethyl ketone, Solvesso No. 2 and

No. 3. Useful solvent mixtures are: 70% acetone and 30% hexane, 97% acetone and 3% mineral oil, 70% turpentine and 30% Hi-flash Solvent Naphtha, 90% Union Oil Solvent No. 30 and 10% xylene. Chlorinated rubber can be dissolved in linseed oil, and other vegetable oils and some of the common plasticizers, such as butyl stearate, dimethyl phthalate and tricresyl phosphate after warming to 100° C. It is compatible with a number of plasticizers and resins. The former include linseed oil, raw castor oil, Aroclor 1242, 1254 and 1260, tricresyl phosphate, tributyl phosphate, diethyl phthalate, dibutyl phthalate, camphor, Hercolyn, Dow plasticizer (5) and (6) etc. The best known resins are: Rezyl 116, Glyptal 2458, 2466, 2500, Beckosol 18, Petrex 1, 2, 3, Bakelite XR3180, etc, Gelva 215, ester gum, dammar, Vinsol, rosin, etc.

Chlorinated rubber is of particular interest as a bonding agent for rubber-metal joints. The technique is comparatively simple; the plasticized solution of the rubber is applied to the metal surfaces, allowed to dry until tacky and then placed in firm contact to ensure effective jointing. A typical formula makes use of ester gum and linseed stand oil with toluene as the solvent.

Imperial Chemical Industries give the following method of bonding Neoprene to metal with their chlorinated rubber (Alloprene B) mixture.

"The surface of the metal (ferrous or non-ferrous) must first be thoroughly cleaned and free from grease. It should then be given three successive coats with a solution of 30 parts weight of Alloprene (grade B) in 70 parts weight of xylene, drying between each application. When the final coats are tacky the surfaces to be bonded are brought into ultimate contact, care being taken to remove all air bubbles by rolling outwards in the usual manner. The built up assembly is then vulcanized. For the best bonds press cures are necessary, but adequate adhesion is obtainable with open steam cures."

Chlorinated rubber adhesives are claimed to be suitable for wax-coated paper. U. S. Pat. No. 2,087,337 specifies a mixture of chlorinated rubber in a suitable solvent heavily loaded with ester gum and waxes. A straight solution of 100 parts low-viscosity chlorinated rubber, 12 parts dibutyl phthalate and 15 parts Aroclor 1260 with 30 parts ester gum or resin in a mixture of turpentine and Hi-flash Solvent Naphtha gives good results.

Adhesives which are prepared with chlorinated rubber as the base are useful on cloth, wood, metal, paper, "Cellophane," leather, cork, and linoleum. Masking and "Cellophane" tapes have also been prepared successfully, using chlorinated rubber. In this application the use of high-viscosity material reduces the necessity of cold flow.

In the preparation of adhesives, Hercules Powder Co. put forward the following suggestions.

### Non-Drying Adhesive

Hercules Chlorinated Rubber (1,000 cp) 2 parts.
Plasticizer                                  1.5 to 3 parts.

### Drying Adhesive

Hercules Chlorinated Rubber (20 or 125 cp) 2 parts.
Plasticizer                          0.5 to 1 part.
Resin                                1  to 3 parts.

## Factors Influencing Success of Chlorinated Rubber Adhesives

1. In preparation always add the chlorinated rubber to the solvent and stir vigorously so as to prevent the formation of a large gelled mass at the bottom of the receptacle.
2. Choose a suitable viscosity rubber for the application.

Generally speaking the lower viscosity grades are the most suitable.

3. Choose a plasticizer and resin that will produce the requisite modification of the rubber film desired for the particular application. Where the film is required to resist chemical attack, the most suitable plasticizer is Aroclor 1254 and the best resins are the phenolics.

Apart from the use of chlorinated rubber as an adhesive it is of interest to note that solutions can be employed to render impermeable textile fibres, leather, paper, wood, sheets of cellulose derivatives, etc. The compound mentioned in Brit. Pat. No. 471,440 comprises a solution in a volatile solvent of chlorinated rubber 25–45%, a resin 15–40%, a plasticizer 15–25% and a wax 10–15%. Dammar, glycerol phthalic anhydride and coumarone resins are specified together with paraffin wax, carnauba wax and spermaceti. Suitable solvents are gasoline, benzene, toluene, xylene and mixtures thereof.

## Synthetic Rubber Cements

It is only natural that with the eclipse of natural rubber as a basis for adhesives, owing to the seizure of the Eastern plantations by the Japanese, considerable attention should be given to the synthetic rubbers now on the market.

## Types of Synthetic Rubber

The most publicized synthetic rubber is the German material Buna which is a co-polymer of butadiene produced from acetylene by I. G. Farbenindustrie. Grades or special types of Buna are available in Germany to fulfil practically all rubber requirements and the range is now so extensive that varieties of Buna may be obtained possessing pronounced rubber-like properties, such as flexibility, elasticity and resiliency, good resistance to swelling and deterioration in oils and solvents, resistance to heat and oxidizing agents, low permeability to gases, etc. Practically all grades can be readily vulcanized and processed on standard rubber machinery.

One of the best known butadiene polymers produced in the United States is Ameripol (B. F. Goodrich Co.). This is now employed in the U. S. A. for the inner tube of flexible hose handling fuel oils, vegetable oils, hydraulic fluid, alcohol, fire extinguishing medium, de-icing fluid, water, glycol, etc., under all temperatures and without swelling or deterioration. Similar to the butadiene polymers and co-polymers are the dimethyl butadiene polymers known commercially as Methyl Rubber (Bayer and Co., Germany) also isobutene polymer, Oppanol, an I. G. product.

Neoprene, the best known and most important British and American synthetic rubber is manufactured in the United States by E. I. du Pont de Nemours and Co., Inc. and in Great Britain by Imperial Chemical Industries, Ltd. Like Buna it is available commercially in a number of different types, including a neoprene latex, and may be readily processed by means of standard rubber machinery and the adoption of familiar vulcanizing processes. Types of neoprene are available for high resistance to solvents, heat, ageing, etc. It is very important to remember that raw neoprene, like natural rubber, must be vulcanized to obtain the maximum mechanical strength. By suitable processing it is possible to obtain just as extensive a range of products as with natural rubber.

Another important grade of synthetic rubber is Thiokol, an organic polysulfide, product of the Dow Chemical Co., U. S. A. It bears no relation chemically to the butadiene polymers such as Buna, Ameripol, etc., or the chloroprene polymer, neoprene, produced from acetylene. Thiokol is a product of the reaction between ethylene dichloride and sodium polysulfide. It possesses exceptionally good resistance to fuel oils and is recommended for hose intended to handle solvents, also for gaskets, etc.

British organic polysulfide is the I. C. I. material, Vulcaplas. This material is not used commercially in its raw form, but is compounded and vulcanized like natural rubber when its inherent properties are fully developed. There is also a German equivalent, Perduren produced by I. G. From petroleum, various types of synthetic rubber are now being produced in the United States, the best known being Butyl Rubber (Standard Oil Company). Chemigum, Goodyear Tire and Rubber Co., is available in the U. S. A., but its composition is not known.

Vistanex is a Standard Oil production somewhat similar to the German material Oppanol. It is unique inasmuch as it remains flexible at −50° C. but becomes permanently softened when heated at 100° C. for long periods. Vistanex Medium possesses high resistance to chemicals but is liable to deterioration when exposed to strong sunlight. It can be compounded with rubber to produce commercially valuable dielectrics. Vistanex Medium itself has a dielectric constant of 2.2 to 2.3, low power factor, good ozone resistance and dielectric strength. The manufacturers claim that Vistanex absorbs only negligible quantities of moisture after total immersion in water for long periods.

Practically all varieties of synthetic rubber may be compounded to form cements suitable for applications similar to natural rubber and particularly for bonding synthetic rubber to synthetic rubber and to metal. The following are the main types of synthetic rubber cements and their characteristics.

## THIOKOL CEMENTS

### "Thiokol" Elastic Cement No. EC-498

EC-498 is a black, Thiokol-base adhesive of about the consistency of a heavy syrup. It is used as a cement for Thiokol and Neoprene impregnated fabrics.

Both surfaces to which the cement is to be applied should be roughened and cleaned with gasoline naphtha. One coat of medium weight should be brushed on each surface. The second coat applied should be allowed to dry for two or three minutes depending on the weight of coat and the area of the surface coated. When a finger is pressed on the coated surface, a print should be made but the cement should not stick to the finger. When bonding, the surfaces should be pressed together firmly.

The bond should be allowed to set for at least 72 hours for maximum strength but a good initial tack is developed when the surfaces are bonded.

If this procedure does not give a long enough bonding range, that is, if the cement dries before the surfaces are bonded, the cement may be reactivated with ethylene dichloride. A very small amount should be brushed on and the surfaces bonded immediately.

EC-498 should not be vulcanized.

The final bond produced with EC-498 will be of high tensile strength, and extremely resistant to oils, greases and petroleum solvents.

A new product EC-570, at present under development, shows some advantages over the above.

### Thiokol A—Sulfur-Sand Cements

The method of making these cements is as follows:

Melt the sulfur and add ½ to 1 and ½% of phosphorous pentasulfide. This eliminates viscosity changes in the molten sulfur with changes of temperature. It is preferred to maintain the temperature at 140 to 150° C. Cut the Thiokol A into thin strips, or similar small pieces, and add to the molten sulfur. Stir (e.g. mechanically) until dissolved. Use 15 to 20% of Thiokol. When making a laboratory batch of about 30 lbs. the time taken to obtain dissolution was 1 to 2 hours.

In this case the Thiokol was thinned out on a laboratory mill and the resulting sheet added bit by bit.

The resulting concentrated solution of Thiokol in sulfur is cast into iron molds holding about 10 lbs. each. If necessary, the molds can be greased to prevent sticking.

The resulting "bricks" of concentrate are taken to the job and added to molten sulfur in a vessel, e.g. with direct firing, to make, say, a 5% Thiokol ultimate mix. Great care must be taken that workmen do not allow local over-heating and burn the Thiokol during this operation, but keep it well stirred. When solution is uniform, sand is added to extend the cement as may be required, e.g. equal parts, a typical formula being

| | |
|---|---|
| Thiokol | 5 |
| Sulfur | 45 |
| Sand | 50 |

The strongest cement was made with about

| | |
|---|---|
| Thiokol | 4 |
| Sulfur | 36 |
| Sand | 60 |

but this depends on the voids in the sand.

The cement is extensively used in the United States for jointing water pipes, tiles of acid pickling tanks and dairy floors, and as a cement in lightning insulators (by Westinghouse). These uses are described in "Thiokol Facts" Nos. 22, 11, 19 and 20 respectively.

The report of the work by Mellon Institute on these cements is in Chemical and Metallurgical Engineering, November, 1934; p. 583.

## Thiokol Latices

Extremely fine suspensions of Thiokol in water have been made, and these are known as Thiokol latices.

Compared with Hevea latex, these dispersions are rather crude, and owing to the higher specific gravity of Thiokol, the dispersion settles instead of creaming. This settling, however, is reversible and the latex may be redispersed readily by stirring and shaking. Mixtures can be made of this latex with other dispersions, including Hevea latex. Thiokol latex is at present being developed in numerous types, but more especially in two varieties namely Thiokol F type and Thiokol N type. The former latex deposits a film similar to Thiokol F, whereas the latter yields a harder, hornier type of material. The F latex film will withstand low temperatures without becoming brittle, but the N is unsuitable below about $-10°F$. The F latex is more generally used for proofing fabrics where a flexible product is required, and in this connection promises to have wide applications.

The initial concentrations of Thiokol latex can be up to 50% by volume, but this is generally too thick for most applications and needs dilution. For this tap water can be used. On the other hand, should more concentrated dispersion be required the latex can be concentrated by evaporation or more simply by allowing it to settle and drawing off the supernatant water.

The latex is slightly alkaline, and has the isoelectric point at a pH value of about 6.0. The alkalinity is due to a very small amount of magnesium hydroxide used as a dispersing agent. The presence of the magnesium hydroxide makes it desirable to store the latex in glass or protected metal containers. The particle size of Thiokol latex is about $3-5\mu$ and the shape spherical. Special methods of manufacture have to be adopted to obtain a particle size of this order. In the manufacture of ordinary (solid) Thiokol, which also temporarily takes the form of an aqueous slurry, the particle size is very much larger and in no way resembles the special latex.

The films deposited from Thiokol latex may be vulcanized

by precompounding the latex in the proper manner, with subsequent heating. Fairly high zinc oxide dosage is advantageous. There are also other methods of assisting in obtaining the best physical properties of the film. Although these are still the subject of research, some preliminary information may be given.

Plasticization of Thiokol in latex form may be accomplished by the addition of about 2–8% of ammonium hydrosulfide (readily made by fully saturating .880 ammonia with hydrogen sulfide). The ammonium hydrosulfide appears to set as a transient plasticizer, and the dried films attain improved physical properties but, of course, require subsequent vulcanization.

Another procedure is to heat the latex for about 1 hour at 70° F. within 4 hours of use. This pre-treatment by heat causes the film subsequently deposited to attain coherency and full physical properties after cure. Heating, at moderate temperatures, with a dispersion of D. P. G., Thiofide, and zinc oxide in the proportions normally used for mill mixing also promotes film formation.

Thiokol latex is readily applied by spraying, for which purpose it is not necessary to use a first class spray gun; something with a cruder aperture is preferable. It may also be spread, dipped or otherwise normally handled.

## Neoprene Cements

In the manufacture of boots and shoes Neoprene proves useful as a latex or solution and owing to the impossibility of obtaining regular shipments of natural rubber these Neoprene cements are in the greatest demand. Latex gives a vulcanized film, and the Neoprene solution a film which slowly cures up, ultimately becoming resistant to oils and solvents. These films do not soften under the influence of heat and, since the particle size of Neoprene is much smaller than that of rubber, Neoprene solutions have a greater penetrative power than similar rubber solutions, giving a tougher bond than rubber. Such solutions can be used for a variety of purposes such as sticking leather to leather, or leather to wood, or leather to rubber, and have a great advantage over films from rubber latex or cellulose, since in the manufacture of boots and shoes one solution will do all jobs and the necessity to keep even pressure on the article for a specified time is eliminated.

## Properties of Neoprene Latex

The following information is given by Dr. C. Falconer Flint of the Imperial Chemical Industries of Gt. Britain. Neoprene latex of 45% synthetic rubber content may be prepared by running chloroprene into a 2% solution of sodium oleate under high speed stirring and allowing the emulsion to stand. After an induction period, polymerization starts spontaneously in the emulsion and, unless controlled by cooling, the temperature rises to boiling point. Low temperature polymerization gives a better and more uniform product. At 50°F. (10°C.) a quantitative yield of the fully vulcanized polymer is obtained in about 10 hours. The speed of emulsion polymerization is about 20 times greater than that of bulk polymerization of chloroprene. The average particle size of this latex is about 0.1 micron, viz. about one-tenth of that of natural latex. Anti-oxidants may be added to the latex to improve the already excellent ageing properties of the Neoprene. In practice, an emulsion of ethyl-$\beta$-naphthyl-amine is preferred, as giving an emulsion of a particle size comparable with that of the Neoprene latex. About 1% of ammonia solution is added to the latex as soon as polymeri-zation is complete, since traces of hydrochloric acid may be liberated during the reaction and might eventually flocculate the latex. The latex of the composition and with additions described is that commonly sold and used. Neoprene latices are also available without anti-oxidants, or with the alkali salts of an alkyl sulfuric acid instead of sodium oleate as the emulsifying agent. These forms, like natural latex, are electro-negative dispersions. An acid Neoprene latex, in which the particles carry a positive charge, is also on the market, being made by the use of an appropiate emulsifying agent to emulsify the chloroprene.

As already indicated, each particle of Neoprene in the latex is vulcanized, and the mobile milky fluid, which is slightly translucent in thin layers, therefore resembles in some respects vulcanized rubber latex. It dries to a light brown transparent film of vulcanized Neoprene. Ageing intensifies this colour to a dark brown, but otherwise has remarkably little effect upon the material. The fully dried Neoprene film shows an elongation at break of about 950% and a tensile strength at break of about 2,500 lbs. per sq. in. This synthetic rubber is greatly superior to natural latex rubber vulcanized under optimuum conditions in resistance to :

Oxidation
Ozone
Heat
Animal oils
Vegetable oils
Mineral oils
Water absorption
Diffusion of gases (e.g. hydrogen in balloons)
Further it will not propagate flame.

Neoprene latex, generally speaking, is compatible with the same dispersed or emulsified compounding ingredients as may be added to natural latex (vulcanizing ingredients, however, need not be added) and similarly is flocculated or coagulated by acids, polyvalent metallic salts and positive dispersions. It dries out more slowly than natural latex, and the films appear to take some time to settle down to their full mechanical strength.

When a film from Neoprene latex is cooled below room temperature, or upon ageing for a considerable time at room temperature it becomes stiffer, more rigid and more leathery than a corresponding rubber film. This tendency to harden or freeze at low temperatures may be counteracted to some extent by the addition of various softeners to the latex before use. By adding to the Neoprene latex a stabilized ammonia-preserved natural rubber latex in such proportions that a dried film contains from 10 to 25% of natural rubber, a soft, flexible film may be produced which has less tendency to stiffen at low temperatures.

## Neoprene Cements

Howard W. Starkweather and Fred. C. Wagner, Ind. & Eng. Chem., Vol. 31, No. 8, 1939, state that "Cements made from Neoprene Type G are slightly less stable than type E, but up to 17% concentrations are still usable after 5 months storage at room temperature. Compounding somewhat reduces the stability of concentrated cements. The addition of sodium thiosulfate during compounding improves the stability of Neoprene E cements. The viscosity of cements for any given solvent or concentration varies with the plasticity of the Neoprene. The variation of the intrinsic viscosity determined in different solvents makes the calculations of molecular weights from this type of data uncertain."

Unvulcanized Neoprene may be dissolved in benzene, toluene, xylene, coal-tar naphtha, carbon tetrachloride, ethylene dichloride, etc., producing cements that have a much higher ratio of solid content to viscosity than rubber cements. The ratio of solid content to viscosity of a rubber cement is greater if the rubber is well broken down before putting in the solvent, but there is no need to mill Neoprene before making it into cements and nothing is gained by so doing. It is, of course, desirable to sheet the Neoprene out thin so that the solvent will cut it rapidly. Gasoline and petroleum naphtha will swell unvulcanized Neoprene but will not dissolve it. Wood rosin, dibutyl phthalate, tricresyl phosphate, pine tar, balata resin, colophony, acrylic resins, Cumar gum, also chlorinated naphthalene and chlorinated paraffin wax may be used as modifying agents. It is claimed that a mixture of 1.5 to 2 parts of colophony and 1 part of silicic acid with one part of synthetic rubber in solvent makes a workable cement.

Synthetic rubber cannot easily be attached to natural or synthetic rubber. An interesting method is given in a British Patent which makes use of an adhesive comprising a solution of a hardening synthetic resin of the phenol-formaldehyde type in ethyl alcohol or other organic solvent to which a solution of ortho, meta or tetra boric acid in an organic liquid, e.g. alcohol, has been added together with a chlorinated solvent. Softening or hardening agents may be added to the solution of adhesive. Chlorinated rubber is, of course, the best known bonding agent for synthetic rubber.

## Other Synthetic Rubber Cements

Perbunan and other well known types of synthetic rubber may be used for making special cements of the solvent type. Polyisobutylene, e.g. Oppanol and Vistanex, is of particular interest as it swells and is soluble in

| | |
|---|---|
| Gasoline | Paraffin wax |
| Benzene | Paraffin oil |
| Toluene | Methylene chloride |
| Xylene | Tetrachloromethane |
| Cyclohexane | Chlorobenzene |
| Mineral oil | Carbon disulfide. |

Workable cements may be produced by soaking the shredded polymer in toluene or xylene for 24 hours, shaking and forming viscous preparations of any desired viscosity. Various inert fillers may be added if necessary. The film is unusually elastic even at temperatures as low as −50° C. As Vistanex is a pure highly polymerized hydrocarbon, it possesses outstanding electrical properties, which remain unaffected by immersion in water. The adhesive is, therefore, of considerable interest to those electrical industries requiring insulating cements.

In the writer's opinion the addition of vinyl resins or the solid polymers of ethylene, e.g. the British material "Polythene" made by Imperial Chemical Industries, Ltd. is useful and improves the stability and electrical properties of the Vistanex cements. In the case of "Polythene," this is insoluble in all cold solvents but soluble in xylene, toluene, carbon tetrachloride, chlorobenzene, turpentine, etc., at boiling point (80 to 120° C.).

## Synthetic Rubber Cements for Miscellaneous Applications

Since the outbreak of war there has been a considerable quickening of interest in these cements and many new industrial applications have been found for them. U. S. Pat. No. 1,969,397, describes the use of an intermediate layer of hydrogenated rubber, which may be taken from natural or butadiene, for the manufacture of safety glass. In one example, in which there is used a hydrogenated polybutadiene rubber, a film of regenerated cellulose is coated on both sides with a solution of hydrogenated polybutadiene obtained by hydrogenating the polybutadiene at about 120° C., so as to produce a polymer having a concentration of 3.5 cyclohexane which will have a relative viscosity of 4.5, by immersion in a 40% solution of hydrogenated rubber in cyclohexane. The coated cellulose film is dried, placed between two glass plates, pressed at 30° C. under a pressure of 20 Kgs per sq. cm.

A further patent, U. S. Pat. No. 2,010,012, specifies a mixed aqueous solution of casein, glue and polychloroprene used in conjunction with a sheet of pyroxylin for safety glass.

For cementing soles to shoes, cements made of Neoprene and other well known types of synthetic rubber are now in use in place of the old type of rubber adhesives. U. S. Pat. No. 2,042,483, mentions the use of a cement of polychloroprene in a volatile solvent which is applied to the sole bottom, the bottom of the outsole and the welt, and allowed to dry into a tacky condition. The cemented face of the outsole is then pressed over the shoe bottom surface, thereby binding the outsole firmly to the bottom of the shoe. U. S. Pat. No. 2,061,296 describes another type of polychloroprene cement for the same purpose.

Numerous kinds of synthetic rubber latices or dispersions such as are described in U. S. Pats. Nos. 1,149,577, 1,671,314 and 1,732,795 find growing uses in industry for similar applications to those formerly found for natural rubber latices.

CHAPTER VIII

# MISCELLANEOUS ADHESIVES

## Alkyd Resin Adhesives (Glyptals)

RESINS formed as the result of the reaction of glycerol and of ethylene glycol with phthalic anhydride and also those subsequently modified by treatment with phenol-formaldehyde and urea-formaldehyde resins, are of interest to the manufacturer of adhesives primarily as additions to cellulose and other bases, but also for making special adhesives for sticking metal foil, etc. to flexible surfaces.

The alkyd resins are available in the following main forms:

Oily, viscous, drying-type resins
Oily, viscous, non-drying-type plasticizers
Air-drying resins in solution form
Non-drying resins in solution form
Soft-sticky resins without solvent
Hard, brittle resins without solvent
Resins in aqueous emulsion form

Characteristics of the alkyd resins of main interest to manufactures are:

Excellent durability
Good colour
Fastness to light
Water resistance
Gloss

84

Of main interest are the air-drying types of resin, high-viscosity in xylene, usually 70% solution, and the low-viscosity undiluted resin. The high-viscosity type represents a material of the highest degree of polymerization and one able to dry very quickly and with a high gloss. The dried film possesses great flexibility and adheres particularly well to metal surfaces.

A solution of the high viscosity resin (70% strength) can be thinned down to the required consistency by the addition of white spirit or turpentine, together with small quantities of butanol or cellosolve. The addition of dipentene is recommended as a safeguard against frosting when the resin is dried under particularly bad conditions.

A varnish suitable for many adhesive purposes can be prepared as follows:

| | |
|---|---|
| Resin solution (70%) | 100 parts |
| White spirit | 50 parts |
| Dipentene | 7 parts |
| Butanol | 5 parts |

Trace of paint drier, such as a cobalt naphthenate.

Such a preparation is suitable for rendering cork gaskets oilproof and waterproof.

Low-viscosity alkyd resins can be modified by cooking with linseed oil, dehydrated castor oil, etc., also ester gum. The procedure is simple: The alkyd resin and oil (with or without the addition of solid resin) are heated to 240–250° C. and maintained at this temperature until the mixture remains quite clear on cooling after being spotted on to a glass plate. After cooling to about 180° C. the thinners and driers are added. The following formula is suggested as of interest for varnish adhesives for metals:

| | |
|---|---|
| Low viscosity resin (50–70 cps. 1:1 in toluol soln.) | 100 parts |
| Dehydrated Castor Oil | 80 parts |

| Linseed Stand Oil | 20 parts |
| Ester Gum | 20 parts |
| White Spirit | 200 parts |
| Cobalt Naphthenate | 0.1 part |

As mentioned earlier, apart from the use of straight alkyd resins, resins modified with a non-drying fatty oil and a phenolic resin are also of interest to the manufacturer of special adhesives. Such modified resins are of particular value for compounding nitro-cellulose cements and it is claimed that nitro-cellulose films containing such resins tend to retain solvent rather longer than films containing many solid resins. The proportion of high-boiling and expensive solvents may, therefore, be reduced. The chief value of the addition of modified alkyd resin to nitro-cellulose preparations is to increase their power of adhesion and to improve the flexibility of the film. When employed it is possible to reduce the proportion of plasticizer normally employed for the nitro-cellulose.

The addition of small quantities of zinc resinate will bring about a noticeable improvement of straight alkyd resin solutions particularly as regards adhesive properties and gloss of hardened film.

## Polystyrene Cements

These are of interest for applications where the highest dielectric strength and low losses, together with a very small water absorption, are primary factors. The dielectric strength of polystyrene foil or film is about equivalent to that of mica, namely 5,500 volts per mil. The power factor has been measured for ultra-high radio frequencies. Polystyrene showed a power factor of only 0.04% at wave lengths of 60 to 150 cm. The material has been used as low loss insulation at wave lengths of 1 to 2 cm. and for infra-red transparent windows at a wave length of 0.005 cm. The water absorption of polystyrene is usually quoted at 0.00 per cent for the standard A. S. T. M. immersion of 48 hours in 25° C. water.

Polystyrene films containing no plasticizer are very brittle but considerable modification of physical properties can be produced by means of various additives, particularly Aroclors. It should be remembered, however, that the addition of a plasticizer usually causes a deterioration of electrical and mechanical properties and resistance to moisture. The proportion of plasticizer must, therefore, be reduced to the minimum, i.e. just sufficient to enable the cement to prove generally workable and the dried film to be flexible. Solutions containing polystyrene as the major non-evaporable component have been advocated as electrical insulating varnishes. Such solutions have been applied as a "dope" for coils in the radio industry.

Modified polystyrene solutions brush easily and level to form a remarkably smooth surface with high gloss. Such coatings adhere well, dry properly, show good abrasion resistance and are very durable.

Typical adhesive solutions particularly suitable for electrical applications are given below :

| | | |
|---|---|---|
| Polystyrene resin, air polymerised form | 5 | parts |
| Aroclor 1254 | 1.5 | parts |
| Toluene | 93.5 | parts |

E. E. Halls, "Plastics," April, 1941, states that the ease of dissolution in solvents and the viscosity of the polystyrene solutions so formed depend largely upon the type of polymerization which has been carried out. He recommends that for high-viscosity low-solid-content adhesives, the air-polymerized form is used; for high-solid-content low-viscosity solutions the high-temperature polymer is resorted to. Halls gives particulars of adhesive solutions used for delicate electrical apparatus, i.e. for moisture-proofing all junctions in telephone capsules between aluminium alloy diaphragm and brass seating and between the waterproof membrane and the cover and case.

*Polystyrol Adhesive Solutions*

| Sample No. | 48 | 49 | 50 | 51 | 52 |
|---|---|---|---|---|---|
| Composition by weight % | | | | | |
| Polystyrene Resin, | | | | | |
| air polymer ............. | 7.5 | 7.5 | 4.0 | .... | .... |
| 150° polymer ........... | .... | .... | .... | 25.0 | 25.0 |
| Coal tar benzene .......... | 91.0 | .... | 95.0 | 70.0 | 20.0 |
| Coal tar solvent naphtha .. | .... | 91.0 | .... | .... | 50.0 |
| Aroclor 1254 ............. | 1.5 | 1.5 | 1.0 | 5.0 | 5.0 |
| | 100.0 | 100.0 | 100.0 | 100.0 | 100.0 |

Polystyrene is soluble in aromatic hydrocarbons, chlorinated hydrocarbons, aliphatic esters and most ketones. It is insoluble in alcohols, paraffin hydrocarbons, vegetable oils and waxes.

## Metallic Naphthenates

Although little attention appears to have been given to the adhesive and film-forming properties of these compounds they are worthy of consideration. Aluminum naphthenate offers considerable possibilities as a thermo-plastic cement when used alone or in conjunction with linseed oil, tung oil, etc. Aluminum naphthenate is a jelly-like, transparent, faintly yellowish material which on warming becomes a viscous fluid. It is soluble in most organic solvents, including drying oils and especially in fatty acids. Solutions of much over 10% in white spirit are extremely viscous, 20% solutions are solid, but much higher concentrations, e.g. 40%, may be obtained by dissolving in a mixture of white spirit plus aromatic hydrocarbons, containing 25% butyl alcohol, which cuts the viscosity.

Methods of preparing solution of aluminum naphthenate are as follows:

(a) In volatile solvents. Cut the solid into small pieces
and put into a completely closed tumbling barrel.
The addition of some butyl alcohol is advisable.
This process of solution is a lengthy one. Alter-
natively, the solvent may be heated to 250–260° F.
by steam in a closed container fitted with a stirrer.

(b) In oil. Heat the aluminum naphthenate and the oil
to 430–440° F. with constant stirring until homo-
geneity is obtained.

The writer suggests that the following formula might be
modified to meet requirements :

5–7% aluminum naphthenate in white spirit.

2–4% tung oil stand oil.

The use of aluminum naphthenate has been suggested as
an additive for glyptal, alkyd and oil varnish adhesives as it
increases the water resistance of the film and acts as an anti-
corrosive agent and film toughener. Approximately 2–3%
on the weight of resin employed in the adhesive is suggested
as suitable, but, if desired, this amount may be increased if
it is thought desirable to increase the viscosity of the adhesive.
Aluminum naphthenate is an economical material to employ
and on this account should be considered as an additive.

## The Aroclors

Aroclor resins adhere strongly to smooth surfaces such as
glass and metal or to smooth varnished or lacquered surfaces.

Monsanto Chemical Company state that the softer Aroclors
are suggested for difficult adhesive problems where a flexible
non-drying waterproof material is necessary. Aroclor adhesives are thermoplastic; are readily applied hot without
solvent; do not require high temperatures for easy application,
and are set immediately upon cooling.

The following are the general physical properties of the most

| Form | Aroclor 1260 Light yellow soft sticky resin | Aroclor 1262 Light yellow sticky clear resin | Aroclor 4465 Yellow transparent brittle resin | Aroclor 5442 Yellow transparent sticky resin | Aroclor 5460 Yellow transparent resin |
|---|---|---|---|---|---|
| Color—NPA | 1.0 Max | 1.2 Max | 1.5 Max | .... | 2.0 Max |
| Acidity—Max (mgm. KOH per gm.) | 0.015 | 0.02 | 0.05 | 0.028 | 0.07 |
| Coefficient of Expansion ....cc/cc/° C. / cc/cc/° F. | .... | 0.000640 (25° C.–90° C.) 0.000355 (77°–194° F.) | 0.000611 (25°–65° C.) 0.000039 (77°–149° F.) | 0.00123 (25°–99° C.) 0.000683 (77°–210° F.) | 0.00179 (25° C.–124° C.) 0.000994 (77°–255° F.) |
| Density—Specific Gravity 25°/25° C. (77°/77° F.) / Pounds per Gallon 25° C. (77° F.) | 1.618–1.629 13.50 | 1.646 to 1.653 13.72 | 1.712 to 1.723 14.28 | 1.432–1.447 11.96 | 1.740–1.745 14.50 |
| Evaporation loss—%—ASTM D—6 Mod 163° C. 5 hrs. / 100° C. 6-hrs. | 0.0 to 0.2 | 0.48 to 0.56 | 0.23 to 0.29 .... | 2.0 0.012 | 0.025 1.51 to 1.71 at 260°–5 hrs. |
| Flash Point—Cleveland Open Cup | None | None | None | 247° C. 477° C. | None |
| Fire Point—Cleveland Open Cup ° C. / ° F. | None | None | None | ∧ 350° C. 662° F. | None |
| Pour Point—ASTM ° C. / ° F. | 26 to 36° C. 79 to 97° F. | 34.9 to 38.0° C. 95 to 100.4° F. | 60–66° C. 140–151° F. | 46° C. 115° F. | .... |
| Refractive Index—D—line—20° C. | .... | 1.6501–1.6517 | 1.664–1.667 | .... | 1.660–1.665 |
| Viscosity—Saybolt Universal Sec. (ASTM—D—88) 210° F. (98.9° C.) / 130° F. (54.4° C.) / 100° F. (37.8° C.) | 70–82 2600–4500 .... | 90–103 00–850 at 160° F. (266° F. or 130° C.) | 92–156 (266° F. or 130° C.) | 313.5 | |

important Aroclors from the viewpoint of the adhesive user.

Aroclors (oils and resins) are easily soluble in most of the common organic solvents and drying oils. The hard crystalline materials are in general less soluble than the Aroclor oils and softer resins. All the Aroclors are insoluble in water.

SOLUBILITIES OF A REPRESENTATIVE AROCLOR (4465) IN SELECTION OF SOLVENTS GIVEN BELOW

| | |
|---|---|
| Carbon tetrachloride | VS * cold and hot |
| Dichlorethylene | VS " " " |
| Ethylene dichloride | VS " " " |
| Monochlorobenzene | VS " " " |
| Orthodichlorobenzene | VS " " " |
| Trichlorethylene | VS " " " |
| Drying oils | VS " " " |
| Esters:—Amyl Acetate | VS " " " |
| Butyl Acetate | VS " " " |
| Cellosolve Acetate | VS " " " |
| Hydrocarbons:— | VS " " " |
| Benzene | VS " " " |
| Gasoline | VS " " " |
| Kerosene | VS " " " |
| Mineral spirits | VS " " " |
| Paraffin | $<5.0$ " S hot |
| Pine oil | S ** " S " |
| Toluene | VS " VS " |
| Turpentine | VS " " " |
| Xylene | VS " " " |

\* VS = Very soluble
\*\*　S = Soluble

CHAPTER IX

# USE OF SYNTHETIC ADHESIVES IN THE MANUFACTURE OF AERONAUTICAL IMPROVED PLYWOOD AND HIGH-DENSITY WOODS

THE term "plastic" aeroplane is a most unfortunate one, creating as it does an entirely false impression. Briefly it can be said that it is a modified or improved plywood construction involving the use of resin bonded veneers formed or moulded over a die. This so-called improved plywood contains from 5 to 10% synthetic resin on a weight basis and this resin may be a thermo-setting compound such as phenolformaldehyde liquid resin or dry gluefilm and urea-formaldehyde resin or a thermo-plastic material like one of the polyvinyl resins. T. D. Perry, Journal of the Aeronautical Sciences, March, 1941, gives a useful summary of the principles involved in moulding plywood for aircraft units.

"The fundamental principle involved is that of using an inflated or deflated rubber bag as one of the halves of a pair of moulding dies. There is not only the saving in matching up a pair of dies where the intermediate distance between halves must be very accurately determined, but in many cases the dies are wholly eliminated and, in any event, rubber bag pressure is of the order of fluid pressure

92

and at substantially right angles to any surface that is under pressure. The Duramold, Timm and Vidal processes all utilize this rubber bag pressure principle."

Several standard processes are described by Perry and of particular interest is the method of moulding half-fuse-lages.

"The inner mould may be made of metal or wood, and if metal, may be provided with heating units. The outer shell must be of sheet metal, substantially semi-cylindrical in shape, and firmly bolted to the base plate on which the inner mould rests. The wood parts to be moulded, may be of veneer or plywood, but must be cut to such tapers that each layer covers the other completely and without laps. These parts must be held in approximate locations by tacks (if a wooden mould) paper or cloth tape, steel bands or wire. A deflated rubber bag, somewhat like an air mattress is placed over the freshly spread wood layers, and the outer shell is dropped over the whole and bolted to the base. The rubber bag is then inflated with air, hot water or steam, and the wood layers are pressed and bonded together as well as to the frame members inserted in the mould." "This method," states Perry, "has been successful in making ply-wood hulls for small boats, using an inside mould of skeleton-ized wood, in which ribs are set flush for bonding to ply-wood."

According to H. W. Perry, Plastics, October, 1940, the Aeromold process adopted by Timm Aircraft Corp. consists of the following operations. Once the design of the aero-plane to be built has been decided upon, rough wooden forms are constructed to the approximate size and shape of each individual part of the craft, and corresponding moulds of exact size and shape are made for moulding the parts under pressure. The former and moulds for making the skin are constructed so that the whole covering of the fuselage is made in two half shells and that of wing panels, ailerons and tail components also made in matching halves like a clam shell. A layer of plywood strips as long as the full length of a form are placed on the form successively, with thick coats of resin applied between them and with the grain of the wood crossed. The last layer is bound down temporarily with tapes and the surface sprayed with resin by means of a spray gun. This rough shape is transferred from the form to a precision mould, where the introduction of pressure approximately 50 lbs. per sq. in. forces the plastic resin throughout the grain and cells of the wood and moulds the material into precise shape and size. There the plastic begins to solidify, giving the half skin definite rigidity, whereupon it is removed and fitted in place on the fuselage rings or wing ribs in an assembly jig with each joint surface saturated with the plastic. When the fuselage, wing panels and other major parts have been fully assembled their entire surfaces are again coated with plastic and they are wheeled on the jigs into the oven and cured for several hours at a temperature of 180 to 250° F. with the heat and humidity carefully controlled.

The latest Duramold process is simple and very efficient, being a modification of the old metal mould method. In principle the new process consists of utilizing a mould made of thin sheet light metal adequately reinforced on its outer surface with wooden bracing or supports on its under surface. The veneers are fitted into the mould interleaving them with sheets of dry gluefilm. When the mould is built up in this way a heavy rubber blanket is placed over the top of the mould and clamped over its edge so as to ensure a perfect contact with the surface and topmost veneer. The whole unit is then wheeled into a large autoclave where it is subjected to steam pressure, 100 lbs. per sq. in. and 300° F. for 10 to 12 minutes (depending on the thickness of the improved wood). One of these autoclaves built at the Grand Rapids, Mich. works of the Bakelite Corp., U. S. A. measures 31 ft. in length by 10 ft. diameter.

Decat "Aviation," May, 1941, mentions that one manufacturer in the United States uses an inside mould which is subdivided into smaller parts. In moulding a wing, a jig is made for all the ribs. On this jig two or more laminations are laid with urea-formaldehyde or other adhesive such as polyvinyl cement in between. The jigs are placed in a rubber bag from which all air is withdrawn. This bag acts as a clamp on top of every wood lamination and curves it to any shape the mould might have. The moulds and ribs are then laid one after another on the spars which are made by the same process. These are again placed in the bag for glueing, and finally the stressed skin, which is made of 31/45 inch mahogany lamination, is laid on top of the ribs and spars which are placed in the rubber bag. Air is withdrawn and the bag is placed in an autoclave in which pressure of 80 to 100 lbs. per sq. in. is applied while the mould is raised to a temperature of about 200° F. depending on the wood used.

Another interesting method makes use of two layers of plywood with a layer of cork sandwiched between. The advantage of this process, according to Decat, is the total absence of spars or ribs, allowing an entire stressed skin for wing or fuselage. To reinforce the cork a thin wire mesh is laid in the middle. The mould is made of a thin metal skin stressed in the airplane principle, with heating tube coming in contact. The countermould is made of a rubber bag of the shape of the inside. The whole wing is made at one time in a single piece including the leading edge reinforcement. The resin used is hot-setting phenol-formaldehyde. The wing comes out of the mould highly polished and needs only to be closed at the trailing edge. A three-ply spruce veneer is used on both sides. So far, only a small wing part, 3 ft. long has been produced. It was able to withstand the weight of five men.

Some interesting details are given in "Modern Plastics" regarding the production of the Langley two-engined plastic plywood aircraft, which, apart from motors and other necessary metal fittings and gear is made entirely of resin-impregnated and bonded plywood. All moulds for the production of fuselage, wings, control surfaces, cowlings, etc., are made of wood, sugar pine. The mode of manufacture is as follows:

"The wood plies are laid on the wooden dies or forms. Depending on the specified ultimate dimensions, as many thicknesses as necessary are applied. Between each layer of wood, resin in solution is sprayed or painted on. Fuselages, wings, spars or other parts built up in this manner are placed in a rubberized bag. Next the bag is deflated by using a vacuum. Placed in a rack in the rubberized bag the parts are cured in a steam jacketed tank using heat and pressure. These are varied depending upon the sizes of the parts and the type of plastic. The length of cure is also determined by the material and type factor. The steam pressure inside the tank, exerted on the entire surface of the parts being cured, supplants the female die of conventional powder mould. When the parts are removed after curing they are ready for assembling with only a minimum amount of finishing."

Some of the American manufacturers of moulded aircraft components use a similar method to that employed in Germany by the Auto-Union A.G. prior to the outbreak of war for the construction of stress-carrying wooden bodywork for cars. The pressure needed for glueing was obtained either by clamps on the assembly jig or by wooden screws, in the case of 8 and 10 mm. plywood, and with nails for the 5 mm. skin. This proved satisfactory in every respect so it is reported. The tenon joints of the frame were safeguarded by wood screws. U.F. glues were used throughout. The Bellanca Aircraft Corp. adopt a method similar to the above only a water soluble P.F. glue is employed containing a quick working accelerator. The assembled or glued unit is finally baked at 140° F.

Choice of resin for bonding is naturally of the greatest importance and, as stated earlier in this chapter, several different resin adhesives have been employed. Although normal hot-cure phenolic liquid resins and gluefilms are quite successful the heat and pressure needed for satisfactory bonding have a most injurious effect on the rubber bag and this has to be renewed fairly frequently. Urea-formaldehyde, although overcoming this disadvantage, does not give such a durable and weather resistant bond as P.F. resins. Thermoplastic cements are quite satisfactory in many ways and they require very little heat; their main drawback is that the adhesive flows at elevated temperatures and under intense tropical conditions it is considered that such flow characteristics would induce undesirable dimensional changes. With the development of low temperature phenol-formaldehyde water-soluble resins the whole process is rendered much simpler and there is no risk of injury to the rubber bag. The bond produced with these resins possesses outstanding resistance to moisture, molds, insects, etc.

The thickness of the laminations for building up the wood for moulding varies, but the Timm Aircraft Corp. uses spruce veneers 1/24 in. thick, other manufacturers plies from 1/48 in. to 1/20 in. and some a good deal thicker. All veneers are conditioned in drying kilns to an optimum percentage of moisture which varies with different processes, but is usually 8–10%.

## Strength Values

The following physical properties refer to several different grades of Duramold grade improved plywood.

| Type of Duramold | Direction of Applied Load | Tension | Compression | Young's Modulus T. and C. |
|---|---|---|---|---|
| 1 | Optimum | 25.75 | 13.95 | 3060 |
| 1 | 90° to optimum | 4.72 | 7.70 | 714 |
| 2 | Optimum | 22.73 | 13.03 | 2730 |
| 2 | 90° to optimum | 7.75 | 8.60 | 1053 |
| 3 | Optimum | 19.69 | 12.08 | 2380 |
| 3 | 90° to optimum | 10.80 | 9.51 | 1395 |
| 4 | Optimum | 16.75 | 11.22 | 2040 |
| 4 | 90° to optimum | 13.87 | 10.40 | 1732 |
| | Shear (optimum) | 10.4 | | |

Values (approximate) given are in lb. per sq. in. divided by 1000 x specific gravity of material.

The ratio of fatigue strength to weight of improved wood is superior to the light metals and according to tests carried out on Duramold, this material is approximately 50% better than 17 ST Duralumin in fatigue resistance based on allowable stress for equal weight per unit area. The facility of the plastic reinforced wood for internal damping (high hysteresis) renders it particularly suitable for use under the most difficult and strenuous conditions of service. Damping of vibration by Duramold is stated by the manufacturers to be five times that of metal. Creep and cold flow are very small indeed in comparison with ordinary resin bonded plywood.

Unlike solid timber such as spruce, used for stressed units (spars), improved plywood has a high ultimate strength across the grain, or indeed, in any direction, and is, therefore, not liable to fail under so-called secondary stresses across the grain. One point of great importance is that the moisture content of the new types of improved woods can be controlled and therefore the dimensional stability of the material is very good.

According to information given by Herbert Chase, "Aircraft Production," Sept., 1939: "In tests against sharp changes in temperature, Duramold panels soaked in water for 2 hours at a temperature of +140° F. and immediately put in an atmosphere of –70° F. have shown no weakening or deleterious change, even after repeated cycles."

James Bond in a paper on the strength of plastic-bonded plywood presented at a joint meeting of the Aviation and Rubber and Plastics Subdivisions of the American Society of Mechanical Engineers, June 8th, 1942, gives the following table of bearing strength tests on plastic-bonded plywood and other materials:

BEARING STRENGH TESTS: LOAD VERSUS DEFORMATION

| Material | Load Causing a Deformation Equal to 4% of the Bearing Pin Diameter on Specimens Conditioned for 96 Hours at | | |
| | 160° F. p.s.i. | 70° F. and 55% R.H. p.s.i. | 70° F. in Water p.s.i. |
| --- | --- | --- | --- |
| Canvas | 32,900 | 32,900 | 26,300 |
| Macerated | 31,800 | 26,900 | 25,900 |
| XX | 36,200 | 23,100 | 26,600 |
| 27 ply | 15,400 | 9,500 | 4,500 |
| 7 ply | 16,500 | 12,500 | 5,600 |
| 3 ply | 9,100 | 8,100 | 3,800 |

Mr. A. Gassner, Chief Engineer of the Duramold Aircraft Corp., U. S. A., states (July, 1940, Modern Plastics):

"In compression-buckling the determining factor is EI value, or the product of modulus of elasticity times the moment of inertia of the member. For aluminum alloy E 10,300,000 lbs. per sq. in., for the mahogany base material (Duramold) E 1,100,000 lbs. per sq. in. But the moment of inertia I is equal to 3/12 for unit length and the thickness "t" for Duramold can be 5.4 times the thickness of the aluminum alloy plate. At the same weight the plastic plywood shell would be more than 2.5 times stronger in compression than the unreinforced metal shell, and it would be by 15 to 20 per cent stronger than a metal shell reinforced by long stringers."

Bomb-bay doors of the American Martin bombers are built-up of resin-reinforced plywood and under load test up to 150 lbs. per sq. in., they show no signs of buckling and the deflection measured under maximum test load is approximately one third of the metal counterpart of the same weight.

## High Density or Superpressed Wood

The skin covering used in the production of large moulded aircraft units is, as carefully explained, an improved plywood whereby the resin greatly reduces the moisture absorption properties, increases resistance to moulds, insects, etc., and modifies the physical properties of the wood, etc. In the case of highly compressed wood the function of the resin is totally different as its main purpose is to lock the wood fibres in the compressed condition and prevent an elastic return to the original volume over a period of time. The resin does not itself improve the mechanical strength of the wood and, indeed, in some cases actually causes a decrease, but the combined action of impregnation and high compression results in the production of a definitely superior and aeronautically suitable construction material.

It should be realized that the pressure employed in the moulding of improved plywood units is relatively low, being in the region of 100–150 lbs. per sq. in., whereas the pressure employed in the manufacture of high-density or superpressed wood is 1,000–1,500 lbs. per sq. in.

Some confusion may, perhaps, exist between resin-bonded

COMPARISON OF RESIN-BONDED PLYWOOD AND HIGH-DENSITY WOOD

| Property | Direction of Stress | BEECH | | | BIRCH | | |
|---|---|---|---|---|---|---|---|
| | | Resin-Bonded Plywood | Improved Wood, 45 Ply | Increase, % | Resin-Bonded Plywood | Improved Wood, 50 Ply | Increase, % |
| Specific gravity | ........ | 0.65 | 0.94 | +45 | 0.67 | 1.00 | +49 |
| Moisture content, % | ........ | 9.0 | 6.0 | −35 | 10.0 | 6.5 | −35 |
| Tensile strength | Longitudinal | 19,900 | 18,300 | −7.9 | 19,600 | 18,200 | −7.3 |
| | Transverse | 1,420 | 3,060 | +115 | 1,070 | 5,450 | +400 |
| Compressive strength [a] | Longitudinal | 8,530 | 19,200 | +125 | 9,950 | 16,300 | +64 |
| | Transverse | ..... | 7,680 | ... | 1,280 | 7,680 | +500 |
| Bending strength [a] | Longitudinal | 18,500 | 31,300 | +69 | 19,900 | 31,300 | +57 |
| | Transverse | 1,710 | 5,120 | +200 | 1,420 | 7,820 | +450 |
| Shear strength [a] | Longitudinal | 2,840 | 4,550 | +60 | 2,840 | ..... | ... |
| | Transverse | 1,560 | 2,840 | +82 | ..... | ..... | ... |
| Modulus of elasticity [a] (+000) | Longitudinal | 2,130 | 2,630 | +23 | 2,280 | 3,060 | +34 |
| | Transverse | 130 | 480 | +278 | 830 | 6,830 | +728 |
| Modulus of rigidity (+000) | Longitudinal | 131 | 213 | +63 | 114 | ..... | ... |
| Water, absorption after 50-hrs. immersion, % | ........ | 38.5 | 8.8 | −77 | 43.3 | 8.0 | −82 |
| Swelling after 50-hrs. water-immersion, % | Thickness | 5.8 | 1.05 | −82 | 5.18 | 1.85 | −64 |
| | Width | 3.5 | ..... | ... | 6.5 | 0.18 | −97 |

a Pounds per square inch.

101

plywood and high density wood. The differences are seen at a glance by referring to the table prepared by L. Klein (The Resinous Products and Chemical Co., Philadelphia, U. S. A.) published in Ind. and Eng. Chem., August, 1941.

High-density wood (some writers call it improved wood) is now being used to a growing extent for aeronautical purposes, particularly for the root of aircraft propellers, spars, braces, webs, ribs, etc.

It should be noted that superpressed wood is utilized for several important parts of the moulded plane, the superpressed units being joined to the other parts by means of resin cements.

The factors influencing the strength of superpressed, high-density or improved wood may be conveniently summarized as follows:

    (1)  Bonding pressure and temperature.
    (2)  Position of laminae.
    (3)  Amount of resin.
    (4)  Thickness of veneers or layers.
    (5)  Condition of veneers.

The first is the most important. It has been found that the optimum bonding pressure is 1,000–1,500 lbs. per sq. in., the actual pressure needed to secure the highest mechanical strength being approximately 1,250 lbs. per sq. in. Figures are given by R. K. Bernhard, T. D. Perry and E. G. Stern (Mechanical Engineering, March, 1940) which illustrate the above statement very well.

Incidentally the properties of the laminated wood are dependent to a large degree upon the bonding pressure, thus when plywood bonded at 800 lbs. per sq. in. is subjected to a maximum fibre stress of 2,000 lbs. per sq. in. for 15 minutes at 122° F., the plastic flow amounts to 10.8% whereas

EFFECT OF INCREASING PRESSURES

| Construction | | Specific Gravity | Moisture Content, per cent | Specific Pressure, lb. per sq. in. | Compression, lb. per sq. in. | Tension, lb. per sq. in. | Shear, lb. per sq. in. |
|---|---|---|---|---|---|---|---|
| A | Solid birch | 0.63 | 12.0 | ..... | 6,200 | 10,100 | 2,020 |
| B | 57/48″ birch | 0.77 | 6.6 | 200 | 8,580 | 12,550 | 7,240 |
| C | 69/48″ birch [a] | 1.05 | 7.7 | 500 | 11,720 | 19,160 | 11,540 |
| D | 81/48″ birch [a] | 1.30 | 8.3 | 1,000 | 14,220 | 25,740 | 16,180 |
| E | 85/48″ birch [a] | 1.36 | 8.7 | 1,500 | 14,270 | 28,490 | 15,910 |
| F | 85/48″ birch | 1.35 | 8.2 | 1,500 | 14,540 | 25,030 | 16,360 |
| | Increase E/A, % | 116 | ... | ..... | 131 | 182 | 688 |
| | Increase E/B, % | 77 | ... | ..... | 66 | 127 | 120 |
| | Increase D/B, % | 69 | ... | ..... | 66 | 105 | 123 |
| G | Solid poplar | 0.42 | 12.0 | ..... | 3,550 | 6,100 | 1,100 |
| H | 77/45″ poplar [a] | 0.82 | 5.3 | 500 | 8,460 | 13,420 | 8,220 |
| I | 105/45″ poplar [a] | 1.32 | 7.7 | 1,500 | 14,540 | 23,570 | 16,460 |
| | Increase I/G, % | 230 | ... | ..... | 310 | 286 | 1,396 |

[a] Cooled 15 minutes under pressure.

at 400 lbs. per sq. in. the flow is 8.5%. In the case of improved or impregnated and compressed plywood the degree of cold flow is largely dependent on the resin content and bonding pressure. The impregnated veneers are able to carry high loads without dimensional change by reason of the peculiar resin structure as distinct from the normal cellulose structure of plywood.

Dealing briefly with factor number 2, it has been found that the optimum position of the veneers is alternate cross layers; this arrangement gives a somewhat lower tensile and compressive strength but a much higher shear value than any other position.

The amount of resin is naturally important—too little prevents effective bonding and is unable completely to prevent an elastic return of the wood to the original volume. On the other hand, too much resin renders the wood brittle and unsuitable for aeronautical applications where a high modulus of elasticity and shear strength are necessary. Using Tego film, Bernhard, Perry and Stern found that single layers gave consistently better results than double ones, at pressures above 500 lbs. per sq. in., but below this bonding pressure, the double gluefilm gave higher-strength materials as shown in the following table.

EFFECT OF LAYERS OF FILM

| Construction | Specific Gravity | Moisture Content, per cent | Film Layers | Compression, lb. per sq. in. | Tension, lb. per sq. in. | Shear, lb. per sq. in |
|---|---|---|---|---|---|---|
| 69/48″ birch a | 1,050 | 7.7 | Single | 11,720 | 19,160 | 11,540 |
| 73/48″ birch a | 1,105 | 6.9 | Double | 13,300 | 19,800 | 14,520 |
| 63/48″ birch | 1,050 | 6.3 | Triple | 12,590 | 16,930 | 12,280 |

a Cooled 15 minutes under pressure.

Thickness of veneers has a considerable influence on the strength value of the wood and veneers 1/48″ appear to have given the best results. A comparison of wood produced from 1/16″ and 1/48″ veneers is as follows:

HIGH DENSITY BIRCH

| Type of Stress | Veneers, Thickness | S. G. | Strength Values, lbs. per sq. in. |
|---|---|---|---|
| Compressive | 1/16″ | 0.72 | 7,890 |
| " | 1/48″ | 1.35 | 14,540 |
| Tensile | 1/16″ | 0.72 | 13,920 |
| " | 1/48″ | 1.35 | 28,490 |
| Shear | 1/16″ | 0.72 | 6,330 |
| " | 1/48″ | 1.35 | 16,360 |

The conclusions reached by Bernhard, Perry and Stern regarding the type of wood used are very interesting. They state that neither poplar nor gum plywood approach birch plywood in their strength, if manufactured under a pressure of 500 lbs. per sq. in. However, poplar and birch superpressed plywood have similar high strength values when manufactured under pressures approaching 1,500 lbs. per sq. in. The strength increases for the same materials varying between 66 and 127 per cent for plywood made under 200 and 1,500 lbs. per sq. in. respectively.

Courtesy of the Resinous Products & Chemical Co.

Tego, a phenol formaldehyde adhesive in dry film form, is interleaved between veneers before hot pressing. After bonding in hot press, the plywood is completely water and fungus resistant.

*Courtesy of the Resinous Products & Chemical Co.*

One of the foremost producers of "prefabricated" homes, Gunnison Housing Co., test joints from each production run. They must withstand prolonged soaking in this very hot water without delamination.

## High-Density or Superpressed Wood for Roots of Aircraft Propellers

The best known types of highly compressed and partially impregnated wood for use in the production of v.p. wooden airscrew is that produced by the Samsonow process. This material, frequently known as "Compreg," is used for the root end and at the scarfed region of the Schwarz wooden airscrew.

The highly compressed wood, Jicwood, produced by the Airscrew Co., Ltd., England, for root formations has the following properties:

| | |
|---|---|
| Tensile strength | 47,000 lbs. per sq. in. |
| Shear strength | 7,400 lbs. per sq. in. along grain. |
| Compression strength | 26,500 lbs. per sq. in. |
| Density | 85.6 lbs. / F$^3$ |
| Modulus of elasticity | 4 to 4.5 x 10$^6$ |
| Impact Izod | 13.6 |

The method of manufacturing Compreg can be divided up into five main stages:

1. The veneers of hardwood (beech, birch, mahogany, etc.), 2 mm. to ⅛ in. thick are conditioned so that the moisture content is standardized throughout. The moisture content naturally varies with different manufacturers, but some work to 10% minimum.

2. The veneers are next passed through a glue-spreading machine containing an alcoholic solution of phenolic resin, colored green to show evenness of penetration. The viscosity of the impregnating solution has to be fixed so that the rate of absorption is carefully controlled.

3. The coated veneers are dried off in a kiln at a temperature which will dry the resin without causing premature polymerization or hardening.

4. The resin coated veneers are stacked up in a large electrically heated press and subjected to a pressure in the region of 1 ¼ tons per sq. in. and temperature varying from approximately 240 to 300° F. Too high a temperature causes case-hardening of the surface of the wood. This means that adhesion between the body of the blade and the root will prove difficult to accomplish.

5. The boards of improved wood are conditioned for several days before use. This permits of the flattening out of stresses set up during compression.

The position or orientation of the fibres influences, or rather governs the ultimate physical properties of the wood.

1. This is made up of sheets with parallel fibres in close resemblance to natural wood. First quality is suitable for all applications where a great resistance to traction and flexion and good dielectric properties are needed.

2. Built up of laminae assembled by crossing the fibres at 90° which means that the resistances are compensated in four directions. This quality has a greater resistance to compression and shearing than the first grade.

3. Consists of successive layers placed with their fibres crossing at 45° so that the resistance is practically the same in all directions.

Of considerable interest is the use of a variable density wood for propellers made by partial impregnation of very thin laminae. The shank has a density of 1.4 and the blade less than 1.0. Airseal and Aircraft Research Co., U. S. A., are now producing blades by means of the Decat process. Quite briefly this consists of building up a blade in a steel mould with partially impregnated veneers.

Pressure is then applied, approximately 2,000 lbs. The

blade is taken out of the mould and coated with a thick phenolic resin which effectively seals the surface.

The improved wood root section is joined to the spruce boards making up the body of the blade with U.F. cold-setting glue or casein. The latter is usually preferred for joining the spruce boards.

## Improved Wood for Electrical and Other Components

Resin-impregnated and compressed wood is being used to a growing extent in the aircraft industry for aerial mast bases, small radio housings, aircraft radio panels and many other parts where high dielectric strength coupled with good mechanical properties are needed. The British material "Permali" manufactured by the New Insulation Co., Ltd., is an excellent example of a material specially developed for electrical work. The laminae of wood vacuum-impregnated with synthetic resin are orientated so as to produce the required properties. Material in which the grains of all the laminae are running parallel is used for parts subjected to a tensile strain or which act as a loaded beam; material with the grains of alternate laminae running at right angles to one another is used where rigidity is required in both directions and this form of the material is also the strongest for resisting compression through its thickness, owing to the interlocking of the fibres. A modification of this form of material, with the grain of succeeding laminae still at right angles to one another but with all the grain disposed at 45° to the main axis, gives the best results from the point of view of the dielectric strength along or across the laminae. A type which is used for building up composite parts such as transformer end rings is built up from segments so cut that their grain is substantially parallel to the tangent of the part.

The mechanical characteristics of Permali with laminae 1/16 in. thick and grain running in same direction are as follows:

| | |
|---|---|
| Tensile Strength | 18,000 lbs. per sq. in. |
| Bending Strength | |
| (perpendicular to laminae) | |
| Equivalent fibre stress at maximum load | 18,000 lbs. per sq. in. |
| Mean Modulus of Elasticity | 2.79 x 10 lbs. per sq. in. |
| Bending Strength | |
| (parallel to laminae) | |
| Equivalent fibre stress at maximum load | 18,000 lbs. per sq. in. |
| Mean Modulus of Elasticity | 2.77 x 10 lbs. per sq. in. |
| Compressive Strength | |
| (parallel to grain and laminae) | 18,000 lbs. per sq. in. |
| Shear Strength | |
| (parallel to grain and laminae) | 2,800 lbs. per sq. in. |
| (perpendicular to laminae, parallel to grain) | 4,300 lbs. per sq. in. |
| (perpendicular to laminae and grain) | 6,000 lbs. per sq. in. |

## Impregnated Wood for Press Tools

The need for a greatly accelerated production of light metal pressings in small series, say 1 to 2,000, has presented a great opportunity for laminated wood press-forming tools. For small quantity production these possess several important advantages over standard hardened steel castings. Although pound for pound the improved wood is more expensive than the metal, in actual production of tools the wood is more economical as pattern making, moulding, etc., are eliminated and blocks of the non-metallic material can be machined straight away after seasoning with ordinary metal working tools, or even wood working tools if special working precautions are taken. It is as well to stress the fact, however, that for long runs, 20,000 or so, the wooden press tools are not suitable, but for the numbers usually required in modern aircraft production they fulfil all reasonable requirements. The average life of an improved press-forming tool is 2,000 to 2,500, but even when the tool shows signs of wear it need not be scrapped as it is possible to build it up for re-use. Tools are constantly being patched up for another lease of life, that is for another 500 to 750 or 1,000 pressings. This rejuvenation is of great importance in wartime when all delays must necessarily be reduced to a minimum.

The above figures refer of course, to cold pressings, but for hot pressings up to 300° C. a good laminated wood tool should be able to produce runs of 500 to 700 without injury. It must be remembered that wood is not a perfectly homogeneous substance like steel and uncertain stresses are liable to be set up in the material. Time must be given for the release of these, otherwise slight deformation may take place.

Another factor of importance in production is that, as laminated wood is less than one fifth of the weight of steel, it requires less labor to handle during machining and also to set up the presses. Now that female labor is being employed to a very large extent in aircraft factories this is a consideration of growing importance.

One great advantage of laminated wood for tool making is that, unlike metal tools, the wooden tools can be modified during production with comparative ease and speed, whereas in the case of steel, changes in design usually entail the ordering of fresh tools. This may mean a delay in production at a time when the services are calling for peak production figures. There is nothing static in aircraft design and modifications rendered necessary by operational or experimental discoveries are fairly frequent. The ideal, of course, is to make every stage of manufacture adaptable so that slight changes in design do not throw everything out of gear.

The orientation or position of the veneers in the wood influences to a great degree its mechanical properties. In the case of improved wood for tools the grain of the laminae are all parallel, thus giving the maximum compressive strength. The figures in Jabroc are 42,000 to 45,000 lbs. per sq. in. (shear strength 11,000 to 17,000 lbs. per sq. in.; specific gravity 1.34 to 1.4).

Both in Germany and in Great Britain the practical advantages of laminated wood for press tools are appreciated and there is a growing demand for the material in the aircraft and associated industries. In "Aircraft Production," August, 1940, there is an interesting account of typical applications of the all-British material Jabroc. According to the above, Jabroc tools are being used very successfully for producing light-alloy diaphragms. In addition to the raising of the external flanges, the stiffening ribs are formed and the lightening holes flanged in the tool at one hit. Both routing templates and forming blocks for the trailing edge rib are made from this improved wood. The routing tools comprise a top and bottom template between which the rough blanks are sandwiched for machinery purposes. Steel bushes are pressed into the top member, which is also used as a drilling template for the various rivet holes required in the web portion of the rib. In the case of this part, the forming blocks are for hand use. The formed block is clamped between the two templates and held securely, while the flange is "knocked up" round the profile with a mallet. This method, it is stated, is sufficiently speedy for small quantities, and has the advantage that the small "return" flange, at the open end of the main flanges, can be formed in the same operation. The lightening holes in the component are flanged separately by a standard tool and the recesses in the blocks are for clearance purposes only. Blanking tools are also being made from Jabroc. In tools of this kind, however, punch and die are faced with a mild steel plate which provides the cutting edge. In forming tools also steel inserts are incorporated in the dies at points where exceptionally heavy wear is to be expected such as on sharp corners or where severe curvatures are required. One of the most interesting jobs allocated to Jabroc tools is the forming of the sump for the Anson fuel tank. It is stated in "Aircraft Production," Sept., 1941, that some 2,000 blanks have already been formed on a Jabroc tool without it showing any apparent signs of wear.

## Improved Wood for Models Intended for Research

True to scale and finely finished models for testing in wind tunnels are now usually made of improved or laminated wood, the veneers being of mahogany, with the various fittings and control surfaces fabricated of metal. According to a published account (July, 1940, "Aircraft Production") of work done in the Northrop tunnel, reputed to be the largest in the United States, the model is suspended by an ingenious system of rigging which permits tests and measurements of lift, drag, sideforce pitch, yaw and rolling movements at the same time. Forces are measured on six Toledo scales simultaneously from one position by the operator, who can lock the scales to get his readings at one time if he desires. Changes in pitch and yaw settings during the test run can be made without shutting down, or removing the model from the tunnel.

## Fan Blades and Propellers of Improved Wood

Airscrew fans for steam and fume removal, ventilation, engine cooling and drying of doped surfaces, etc., are now being made either wholly or partially of improved wood. In the case of the metal airscrew fan of the high efficiency axial flow type with blades of airofoil section, it is quite a common practice to use a laminated wood impeller. This conserves the national use of essential metal, is lighter, better balanced and more resistant to atmosphere-acid than a metal impeller. The veneers of hardwood used for the manufacture of improved wood are either impregnated with an alcoholic solution of phenolic resin and bonded together under heat and pressure, or sheets of dry gluefilm are placed between the veneers and the pile subjected to heat and pressure in a daylight press to form a new kind of compressed wood. Both compressed and impregnated woods are utilized for this comparatively new industrial development.

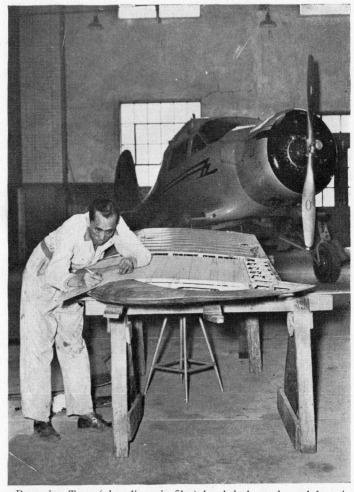

Preparing Tego (phenolic resin film) bonded plywood panel for wing of Beechcraft airplane. Resinous Products & Chemical Co., Philadelphia, Pa., U. S. A.

# Chapter X

# GENERAL APPLICATIONS OF SYNTHETIC ADHESIVES IN INDUSTRY

| Industry | Application | Type of Resin | Main Advantages |
|---|---|---|---|
| Woodworking | Aeronautical and general utility plywood. | Dry phenolic gluefilm: e.g. Tego. Liquid phenolic glue. Alcoholic and aqueous solutions urea-formaldehyde glues and vinyl cements. | 1. Very high mechanical strength. 2. Resistance to moisture. 3. Immunity to attack by fungi and insects. 4. Permanent and non-ageing properties. 5. Non-staining. |
| Woodworking | High density or superpressed woods: root of aircraft propeller; spars; braces; webs; ribs, etc. | Tego film. Liquid phenolic glues. | 1. Outstanding mechanical and physical properties. 2. Great resistance to moisture, fungi, insects. 3. Suitability for applications involving high operational stresses and strains. |
| Woodworking | Assembly of wood units in the aircraft industry, also in shipbuilding, furniture trades and building. | Urea-formaldehyde cement. | 1. Very high strength and durability under stress. 2. Immunity to fungi and insects. 3. Low temperature and pressure of bonding. 4. Low water content of glue and freedom from twisting or distortion. |

*Continued*

| Industry | Application | Type of Resin | Main Advantages |
|---|---|---|---|
| Boot and Shoe Trade | Cementing leather to leather; leather to wood; leather to rubber and fabrics. | Rubber (natural and synthetic) latices and cements (solvent); nitro-cellulose and polyvinyl cements. | Synthetic rubber latices and solvent solutions are superior to many natural rubber adhesives owing to greater penetration and tougher bond. Nitro-cellulose and vinyl cements can be readily modified to meet new machining requirements. |
| Rubber | Bonding rubber to rubber (natural and synthetic); rubber to wood and rubber to metal and ceramic materials. | Synthetic rubber and chlorinated rubber cements; also acrylic resins. | Better adhesion, greater strength and durability of bond than is possible with natural rubber. |
| Chemical Industry | Cements for lining and pointing silicate cement and brick lined vats, towers, etc.; jointing of metal and ceramic units. | Specially compounded (heavily filled) phenolic cements containing acid catalysts; also synthetic rubber "Thiokol" cements and vinyl "Koroseal" cement. | 1. Good adhesion. 2. Ability to withstand continuous contact with corrosive chemicals. 3. Excellent durability under service conditions. |

*Continued*

116

| Industry | Application | Type of Resin | Main Advantages |
|---|---|---|---|
| Textile | Thermo-plastic adhesive for general applications where resistance to hot laundering conditions allowed. | Acrylic resin and vinyl cements. Chlorinated rubber base adhesives. | 1. Excellent adhesion. <br>2. Resistance to moisture. <br>3. Great flexibility and resistance to flexing, etc. <br>4. High degree of permanence. |
| Paper | General sizes in wall paper and bookbinding trades. | Methyl cellulose and acrylic resins, particularly the dispersions in water. Chlorinated rubber base adhesives. | 1. Good adhesion. <br>2. Excellent resistance to fungi and bacteria. <br>3. Stability of made-up sizes. <br>4. Ease of preparation. |
| Food | Thermo-plastic and heat sealing adhesives for many different types of packaging, i.e., transparent and opaque wrappings. | Ethyl cellulose, polyvinyl and cellulose ester cements. Modified cellulose adhesives for sticking waxed paper. | 1. Odorless and tasteless. <br>2. High degree of adhesion. <br>3. Colorless and non-staining. <br>4. Resistance to humidity and moisture. <br>5. Resistance to fungi and bacteria. <br>6. Economy in use. |
| Photographic | Mounting of photographic prints, etc. | Polyvinyl acetate (Gelvas) in the form of foils, also synthetic rubber cements, e.g. Vistanex. | 1. Good adhesion. <br>2. Non-staining. <br>3. Resistance to moisture. <br>4. Resistance to mould. |
| Medicinal | Protective skin dressings. | Ethyl cellulose. | 1. Good adhesion. <br>2. Non-toxic. <br>3. Ease of application and removal. <br>4. Promotes healing. |

*Continued*

117

| Industry | Application | Type of Resin | Main Advantages |
|---|---|---|---|
| Electrical | Lamp base cements; varnishes for general joining work; special high dielectric adhesives for radio work. | Phenolic (baking) cements. Polystyrene solvent solution for radio and television work. | 1. Good adhesion. 2. Excellent insulating properties. |
| Plastics | Joining moulded or laminated surfaces. | Polyvinyl and acrylic resin cements; also new type of urea-formaldehyde resin. | 1. Good adhesion. 2. Adequate strength of film. |
| Brush Making | Bristle setting cements. | Phenolic (baking) cements. | 1. High degree of adhesion. 2. Permanence under severe service conditions. |
| Manufacture of Artificial Leather | Bonding together leather scrap, paper pulp, etc. | Neoprene latex. Chlorinated rubber base cements. | 1. Tensile strength of film high. 2. Durability good. 3. Resistance to freezing good. |
| Linoleum | Replacement of natural gums and glues for bonding purposes. | Polyvinyl and acrylic cements. Chlorinated rubber base cements. | 1. Improved adhesion. 2. Great strength of bond. 3. Greater permanence in service. |
| Cork and Gasket Manufacture | Bonding and impregnation of cork granules for oil-resisting gaskets. | Neoprene latex. | 1. Excellent adhesion. 2. Quick drying time. 3. Resistance to freezing at normal low temperature. 4. Resistance to oils. 5. High tensile strength. |

*Continued*

| Industry | Application | Type of Resin | Main Advantages |
|---|---|---|---|
| Hydraulic Cement | Manufacture of flooring sealing compounds. | Neoprene latex. | 1. Durability. <br> 2. Strength of bond adequate to resist effects of wear. |
| Glass (Safety) | Production of safety laminated glass. | Polyvinyl acetate and polyvinyl acetal plastic extensively employed. | 1. Great adhesion. <br> 2. Good clarity. <br> 3. Resistant to the discoloring effect of U.V. light. <br> 4. Ability to stretch and yield under sudden impact. |
| Abrasives | Bonding together abrasive particles to form cutting wheels, etc. | Phenol-formaldehyde resin. | 1. Great adhesion. <br> 2. Resistant to high friction heat. |

# INDEX

121

Perduren, 73
Permali, 109
Phenol adhesives, special, 19
Phenol-formaldehyde glues, 11
Phenol-formaldehyde resin, 1
Phenolic baking cements, 17
Phenolic glues for aeronautical applications, liquid, 16
Phenolic glues, methods of application, 12
Phenolic glues, water-soluble, 13
Phenolic resin cement, 18
Phenolic resins for compressed wood, aqueous solutions of, 15
Phenolic resins in powder form, 16
Phenolic resin putty, 18
Phenolic resin rubber cements, 18
Photographic industry, synthetic adhesives in, 117
Physical constants of Gelvas, 56
Physical properties of Aroclor adhesives, 90
Plasticizer for cellulose esters, 40
Plasticizers for ethyl cellulose, 48
Plasticizers for polyvinyl adhesives, 56
Plastic plywood, strength of, 98
Plastics, synthetic adhesives in, 118
Plywood, effect of pressure on properties of, 103
Plywood, tests on plastic-bonded, 99
Plywood, urea-formaldehyde bonded, 24
Poly-*n*-butyl acrylate, 63
Polychloroprene cement, 83
Polyethyl acrylate, 63
Polymethyl acrylate, 63
Polystyrene cements, 86
Polystyrol adhesive solutions, 88
Polyvinyl adhesives, methods of applying, 57
Polyvinyl adhesives, plasticizers for, 56
Polyvinyl adhesives, solvents for, 56
Polyvinyl alcohol, 60
Polyvinyl cements, 54
Polyvinyl chloride, 59

Polyvinyl resin adhesives, requirements of, 58
Powdered phenolic resins, 16
Pressing conditions of dry glue-film, 3
Pressing urea-formaldehyde bonded wood, 28
Press tools, impregnated wood for, 110
Propellers of improved wood, 113

R

Requirements of polyvinyl resin adhesives, 58
5116 Resin Adhesive, 19
Resin-bonded plywood and high-density wood, comparison of, 101
Resins compatible with cellulose esters, 37
Rubber industry, synthetic adhesives in, 116
Rye flour for extending urea-formaldehyde glue, 27

S

Safety glass, 47, 54, 59, 61, 82
Safety glass manufacture, synthetic adhesives in, 119
Shear tests of urea-formaldehyde bonded plywood, 24
Shoe trade, synthetic adhesives in, 116
Solid phenol-formaldehyde glues, 11
Solubility of Aroclor 4465, 91
Solvents for cellulose ester cements, 38
Solvents for chlorinated rubber, 68
Solvents for ethyl cellulose, 46
Solvents for Neoprene, 80
Solvents for polyvinyl adhesives, 56
Solvents for synthetic rubbers, 81
Special phenol adhesives, 19
Spreading of urea-formaldehyde glues, 26
Strength of plastic plywood, 98